Food Safety Code of Practice

For Canada's Foodservice Industry

Canadian Restaurant and Foodservices Association

2009 Edition

Notice to Readers

The Food Safety Code of Practice is a practical guide to understanding and implementing the principles outlined in the model Food Retail and Food Service (FRFS) Regulation and Code as developed by the Canadian Food Inspection System Implementation Group (http://www.cfis.agr.ca). Every effort has been made to ensure that the information contained in this manual is accurate and complete at the time of printing. However, readers should be aware that the FRFS Regulation and Code may be revised from time to time or revoked without notice. Furthermore, this document does not constitute a legal interpretation of the requirements of the FRFS Regulation and Code and the Canadian Restaurant and Foodservices Association (CRFA) does not provide any such interpretations.

The CRFA, its members and those participating in its activities do not accept any liability resulting from compliance or noncompliance with the FRFS Regulation, Code, or the Code of Practice herein.

Readers should be aware that the CRFA does not monitor or enforce compliance with the contents of this document. Any self-declaration of conformity or certification by a third party stating compliance with the requirements of this document or the FRFS Regulation and Code is at the sole responsibility of the individual or company making the statement. It is assumed and intended that consumers will exercise appropriate personal judgement and responsibility and that restaurant owners will create and enforce rules of behaviour and warnings appropriate for their managers, employees, and establishment.

Canadian Restaurant and Foodservices Association
316 Bloor Street West
Toronto, Ontario
M5S 1W5
(416) 923-8416 WWW.CRFA.CA

We would like to extend our sincere appreciation to Agriculture and Agri-Food Canada and the Canadian Food Inspection Agency through the Canadian Food Safety Adaptation Program for their financial support of this project.

ISBN: 978-0-9811878-0-8

Table of Contents

Table of Contents

Section I
Introduction

I. Introduction

1. What is the Code of Practice?

The Code of Practice is an interpretive guide that strives to make it easy for every restaurant owner, manager, and employee to access, understand and ensure customer food safety.

Top Ten Commonly Asked Questions:

1. Q: What are the most frequent causes of foodborne illnesses?
   A: See Appendix H - Major Foodborne Illnesses on pages 156-159.

2. Q: What should I do if someone calls with a food safety complaint?
   A: See Appendix F - How to Respond to Suspected Foodborne Illness on pages 153-154.

3. Q: Should a sick or injured employee work with food?
   A: See Section VIII - 1. Illness and Disease on page 120.

4. Q: What is expected from employees regarding hygiene and sanitary practices when handling food?
   A: See Section VIII - 3. Employee Hygiene on page 121.

5. Q: What are acceptable methods for sanitizing silverware and dishes?
   A: See Section VI - 1. Cleaning Program for Facilities and Equipment on page 104.

6. Q: What should I do if I find food contaminated by mice or insects?
   A: See Section VII - 1.2 Pest Control on page 115.

7. Q: How do I calibrate a thermometer?
   A: See Appendix C – Thermometer Calibration on pages 149-150.

8. Q: What type of training do food handlers need?
   A: See Section IX - Food Training Programs on page 133.

9. Q: What are appropriate storage and receiving procedures?
   A: See Section IV - Storage and Receiving on pages 68-74.

10. Q: What are food allergens and how do I control them?
    A: See Section II - Allergens on page 30.

Consumers are more concerned about food safety issues than ever before. The Canadian foodservice sector and government have responded by ensuring that a set of common food safety practices is shared throughout Canada. This was done through the joint creation of the Canadian Food Retail and Food Service Model Regulation and Code. The Canadian Restaurant and Foodservices Association (CRFA) supports the adoption of this Regulation and Code across Canada.

The following Code of Practice is a practical guide to understanding and implementing the national FRFS Code and its model regulation. In some cases, examples have been provided to show how the requirements of the Code can be met in a number of ways. This Code builds on the strengths of CRFA's Sanitation Code and incorporates technical changes that have taken place in food preparation, processing and service. This Code of Practice also assists foodservice establishments in understanding the "risk management approach" required by Hazard Analysis and Critical Control Point (HACCP) programs.

Simply, the CRFA Food Safety Code of Practice is designed to help foodservice operators manage food safety risks.

2. Why is the Code of Practice Important to Foodservice Operators?

Many people experience foodborne illness each year. Annually, as many as 11 to 13 million Canadians develop foodborne illness, nearly 39,000 people are hospitalized, and as many as 600 die. Food poisoning and other types of food related illnesses cost our healthcare system as much as $2 billion annually. Most cases of the "24-hour flu" are in fact foodborne illness. The average person in Canada may become ill from food as many as 15 times in his or her life.

You might ask, "If foodborne illness is so common, why don't we hear about it more often from our customers, in the news or from health authorities?" Only 1 in 10 cases of foodborne illness is reported to health care authorities. Since most cases go undiagnosed, they are not tracked or reported. Therefore, foodborne illness has been largely overlooked in the past.

What has changed? Increased sampling and testing of food products, DNA fingerprinting of "illness-causing" bacteria, and high-profile food and waterborne illnesses in Canada and the United States have placed a spotlight on foodborne illness. Governments and consumer groups are now requiring farmers, food processors, retailers and foodservice operators to increase their diligence around the management of food safety.

Foodborne illness can be devastating to any part of the food industry, including foodservice operations.

Past incidents of food poisoning have resulted in:

- Death and serious illness involving young children and other customers.
- Permanent closure of food operations, or significant loss of earnings due to temporary closure or negative publicity.
- Law suits and associated high monetary costs including: lawyer fees, payouts to complainants, lost business due to bad publicity and stress on management.
- Poor customer service due to discouraged staff and high employee turnover.
- Professional embarrassment.
- Personal feelings of grief and regret, associated with killing or seriously injuring a customer.

Preventing foodborne illness is at the heart of Hazard Analysis and Critical Control Point (HACCP) programs. These programs focus on critical factors that prevent and manage the risk of foodborne illness. This Code of Practice outlines the principles of HACCP. CRFA has developed an accompanying Food Safety Tool Kit that will help operators to understand and implement HACCP-based programs in their foodservice operations.

The good news is foodborne illness and its associated results are preventable. This Code of Practice is a practical tool for foodservice operators who want to manage these food safety risks and helps protect their customers.

3. How Should a Foodservice Operation use this Code?

This Code of Practice has been designed to provide the "whats", "whys" and some of the "hows" required to effectively manage food safety. The Code specifies:

> **"What"** is required in the construction, daily operations, and training in a foodservice establishment.
>
> **"Why"** these things are important to food safety management.
>
> **"How"** some of these requirements can be practically met. The Canadian Restaurant and Foodservices Association's Food Safety Tool Kit will provide further detailed steps on "how" food safety can be managed through these programs.

For an establishment to operate in line with this Code of Practice every day, everyone in the organization must use it frequently. The Code of Practice can provide guidance:

1. When making changes to physical facilities, such as the kitchen, so modifications in premises design and equipment are made with food safety in mind;

2. When adding new ingredients or menu items, to ensure that all food safety hazards have been fully controlled;

3. To foodservice employees to confirm safe cooking, chilling, hot holding, and reheating practices;

4. For training new employees and providing refresher training for existing employees;

5. When dealing with suppliers such as pest control contractors, sanitation chemical companies and food sales agents;

6. During audits and inspections by regulatory agencies; and

7. When conducting routine internal audits and staff performance reviews.

Finally, throughout this Code certain requirements have been identified as "Must Do" or "Highly Recommended" to help distinguish between absolute requirements (Must Do) and highly recommended practices (Highly Recommended) in the Food Retail and Food Services Regulation and Code model. These requirements have been highlighted within a box and have the marks (MD) or (HR) placed in the left-hand margin. The italicized paragraphs below the boxed areas describe why these requirements are important. The descriptive bullets and paragraphs that follow describe how you might meet these requirements.

MD

Highlights "Must Do" practices. These are absolute requirements of the Food Retail and Food Services Regulation.

HR

Highlights "Highly Recommended" practices that are not absolute requirements of the Food Retail and Food Services Regulation. If applicable to your foodservice operation, they are the best practices for food safety.

1

A Step-Wise Approach to Using this Code of Practice

1. Start by reading the section on "Food Safety Hazards". This will help your understanding of why the "Must Dos" are important.

2. Read this Code of Practice and make a list of the "Must Do"(MD) requirements that apply to you.

3. Audit your operation to ensure that the MD items are in place.

4. Make a list of MD items that are missing in your facility and Highly Recommended (HR) practices that are appropriate for your operation.

5. Create a plan of action that will ensure that all missing MD items are put in place over a specified period of time. This plan may include the development and/or implementation of record keeping systems, standard procedures or activities.

6. Discuss the MD items with your staff. Explain why these items are important and get their input about how they can help implement these requirements.

7. Execute your plan of action and review the list of "Must Do" items every three to four weeks to determine if any changes in equipment, facilities, people, menu items or external services have created any unmanaged food safety risks.

Foodservice operations should promote daily awareness of this Code of Practice within their organization. It should be used for everything from facility design to training. Frequent reinforcement of its content among employees will allow everyone to form good food safety habits. Through awareness, understanding and routine implementation of this Code of Practice, foodservice operations will be able to effectively manage their food safety risks.

Section II
Food Safety Hazards

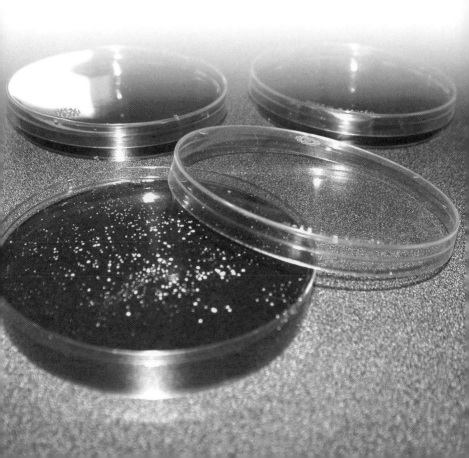

II. Food Safety Hazards

The purpose of any food safety management program is to prevent food safety hazards from coming in contact with the food served to customers.

There are four general types of hazards in food that can cause death, illness and injury to consumers.

1. Biological – including parasites, viruses, bacteria, and moulds.

2. Physical – including glass, metal, wood chips or jewelry; anything that can cause choking or internal injury.

3. Chemical – including cleaners, sanitizers, pesticides and paint; any chemical that can make the food dangerous to eat.

4. Allergens – including fish and shellfish, tree nuts and peanuts, eggs, dairy products, sulfites, soy products, sesame seeds and wheat.

---

1. Biological Hazards

These hazards are called "biological" hazards because they are living organisms that can grow. They include parasites, prions, viruses, bacteria and moulds and individually are so tiny you require a microscope to view them. For example, several million bacteria can fit on the head of a pin. Because these organisms are so small, they can hitch a ride on everything from dust particles in the air to our clothes, hands, face and footwear. For this reason they can spread very quickly throughout a foodservice operation from an insect to a cutting board, from the cutting board to a food product, from the food product to the customer.

Parasites:
Parasites are small organisms that live in animals or humans. Unclean water can contain parasites such as protozoa, Cryptosporidium or Cyclospora, which can cause food poisoning in humans. Food poisoning occurs when this water is used to irrigate or wash fruits or vegetables that may not be fully cooked before consumption.

2

A Case in Point

In 1996, over 1400 people got food poisoning from fresh Guatemalan raspberries that were carrying a parasite from the Cyclospora family. Since raspberries cannot be easily washed, it was not possible to remove the parasite and the raspberries had to be recalled from the fresh market. People had the symptoms of diarrhea, fever, nausea, vomiting, abdominal pains and chills.

The Problem:
Inspectors found that the berries were being harvested and packed by farm workers testing positive for Cyclospora. It is likely that the workers were infected by untreated drinking water. Sources of this parasite include water in which animals and birds were allowed to drink, bathe and defecate. This water is then used for irrigation, spraying fungicides and other substances on the fruit.

Solution:
It is important for ready-to-eat fruits and vegetables that are not easily washed to be produced, harvested, handled and transported under very clean conditions. This parasite can be deadly for anyone who is already sick with a long-term illness such as AIDS.

Prions:
Mad Cow Disease or Bovine Spongiform Encephalopathy (BSE) in cattle has been strongly linked to a disease in humans called new variant Creutzfeldt-Jakob disease (nvCJD) through small proteins called prions. These prions cause a deadly brain disease in cattle and humans. Eating some parts of cattle, such as

specified risk materials (i.e. brain tissue) from an infected animal may cause a type of nvCJD in humans. While BSE has been detected in North America, Canada actively monitors for the disease and has programs in place to prevent specified risk materials from getting into the food and feed chain.

Bacteria, Moulds, and Viruses (Microorganisms)

What effect do microorganisms have on people and food?
Some types of microorganisms such as bacteria, moulds and viruses can cause food poisoning. Not all microorganisms are dangerous. In food products, microorganisms may have four possible effects:

i) Inert: are present in food but do not affect people and do not cause food poisoning;
ii) Beneficial: are useful in food products and perform a specific function such as fermentation, which is used for making cheese and fermented sausage, and yeast which is used for making beer;
iii) Food spoilage organisms: can cause food to spoil, but do not make us sick and;
iv) Pathogenic: can cause illness and sometimes death in humans. Pathogenic bacteria cannot be seen without a microscope. They grow by absorbing the available food around them and can double at room temperature every seven to 20 minutes. This means that one bacteria can multiply to unsafe levels in just over two hours. Confusion can occur because some food items may look and smell fine but be unsafe for consumption due to the presence of pathogenic bacteria.

How do microorganisms make people sick?
Pathogens are the major concern for food safety programs. They can make people sick through two ways:

i) Infection: The microorganisms invade the human body and grow in the human intestine. Once infected, the body tries to reject the infection. The incubation period (time of infection to time of illness) is usually 12 to 48 hours depending on the pathogen. People may be sick from one day to a week. Symptoms may include fever, headache, nausea, vomiting, cramps and dehydration that can lead to death. Some microorganisms can cause additional illnesses. For instance, Listeria Monocytogenes, a pathogen found in refrigerated foods, can attack the brain and cause meningitis, an infection of the lining of the brain.

ii) Intoxication: The microorganisms produce a poison or toxin in the food. Once the poison or toxin is ingested, a person can become sick in two to eight hours. The duration of the illness varies, but may run for 24 hours. The symptoms may include headache, nausea, vomiting, cramps and dehydration and can result in death. In some cases, the toxin can affect the nervous system causing double vision, dizziness, muscular weakness and in the most severe cases respiratory failure and death. For instance, an organism called Staphylococcus Aureus, found on the hands and face of approximately 40% of the population, can produce a toxin in food if the food is contaminated and is not kept properly refrigerated.

2

A Case in Point

A Canadian catering company made sandwiches for members of a police force who were providing crowd control for a dignitary. The food handlers carried Staphylococcus aureus on their hands and did not properly wash their hands or wear gloves when making the sandwiches. The sandwiches were not kept refrigerated (4°C / 40° F) during the six to eight hours from the time they were prepared to the time they were eaten. The Staphylococcus Aureus toxin was produced in the sandwiches. Although the sandwiches looked and smelled acceptable, a large number of the officers were stricken with food poisoning several hours after eating their lunch.

The Problem:
Employees can carry pathogens such as Staphylococcus aureus on their hands, face and in their hair. The sandwiches were not kept refrigerated. This allowed the Staphylococcus aureus to grow and produce a toxin.

> Solution:
> Hands should always be thoroughly washed to remove soil and bacteria. It is often advisable to also wear plastic or vinyl gloves when directly handling food.

Where do microorganisms come from?

Microorganisms are everywhere! They cannot travel from place to place on their own, but they hitch a ride on living and non-living things. Microorganisms can easily be transferred by:

- One person touching another, through such things as a handshake;

- One person coughing or sneezing on another person, or on any surface that food could touch;

- Dirty clothing, hairnets, or shoes;

- Dirty water splashing from floors, overhead pipes, dripping refrigeration units or air conditioners;

- Rats, mice or insects, which can carry millions of microorganisms onto clean surfaces;

- Dirty equipment that is improperly washed and sanitized; and

- Dust and dirt floating through the air.

A Case in Point

Fried rice at two day-care centres caused 14 children and staff to become sick with abdominal cramps and diarrhea within two hours of eating the product. The rice had been cooked the night before and cooled at room temperature before being refrigerated. On the morning of the lunch, the rice was pan-fried in oil with pieces of cooked chicken. It was delivered to the day-care centres at approximately 10:30 am and held without refrigeration until noon when it was served without reheating.

The Problem:
B. cereus is frequently found in uncooked rice. Heat stable spores may survive cooking. If cooked rice is held at room temperature, the spores turn into growing bacteria and can produce a heat stable toxin. In this case, the spores were allowed to turn into growing bacteria the night before and many bacteria survived the frying process the next morning. Additional bacteria grew and produced the toxin as it sat unrefrigerated before lunch. The rice was tested and found to have one million bacteria per gram!

Solution:
The rice should have been cooled to 4°C (40°F) or lower as quickly as possible. A one to two inch deep container is ideal to cool and hold rice.

2

Moulds:

Most people are familiar with how moulds can spoil food. Moulds are often visible to the naked eye as fuzzy or powdery patches. They like wet conditions and can grow at refrigeration temperatures. Some moulds can produce a toxin in the food that will make people sick. Moulds have invisible filaments that can reach down into the product and inject a toxin as much as two inches below the surface of the product. Therefore, it is wise to remove at least two inches of the product from where it has come in contact with the mould.

Moulds need oxygen to breathe and will not grow in vacuum-packed products, as long as the package is sealed and the vacuum remains intact.

Viruses:

These are the smallest of all the microorganisms. They must invade a living organism such as a person, animal or bacterial cell to grow and survive. Unlike bacteria and moulds, viruses cannot multiply in food. However, they are important because they can be transported in food. For instance, a food handler or server with hepatitis or a viral diarrhea can spread the viruses to the food served or to food contact surfaces, infecting the customer and thus resulting in foodborne illness. Some viruses can survive freezing and normal cooking temperatures.

How can microorganisms be controlled?

Microorganisms need six conditions to live and thrive.

FATTOM:

i.   Food;
ii.   Acidity/pH;
iii. Temperature;
iv. Time;
v.   Oxygen/presence or absence of air; and
vi. Moisture.

I. Food

Like any living thing, microorganisms would die without food. Many microorganisms thrive on the same food as humans. So the foods that we enjoy in restaurants are the very same foods in which microorganisms grow and multiply. They thrive on protein foods such as meat, poultry, dairy products and eggs.

Key Points of Control

- Foodservice operations should only purchase food from an authorized supplier.
- Train employees to understand microorganism growth and how to minimize cross-contamination between menu items.
- Wash food contact surfaces, utensils, pots, pans and service ware thoroughly to minimize cross contamination.

II. Acidity

Most microorganisms usually do not grow in foods that are highly acidic (pH of 4.6 or less) or highly alkaline (pH of 7.5 or more). Fruit juices, salad dressings and spaghetti sauce are examples of foods that are preserved due to a low pH. Egg whites do not support the growth of microorganisms because of a high pH. Products such as milk, meats, fish and egg yolk easily support the growth of pathogenic bacteria because they have a pH between 4.6 and 7.5.

Key Points of Control

- Products with pH between 4.6 and 7.5 should be kept refrigerated.
- Always follow label storage instructions on packaging. Many products, regardless of their pH, should be refrigerated after opening.
- A dangerous pathogen called E.Coli 0157:H7, can survive in low pH products. Food poisoning has occurred in freshly squeezed or unpasteurized apple juice and orange juice. Do not depend on acidity alone to preserve a product.

2

pH of some common foods

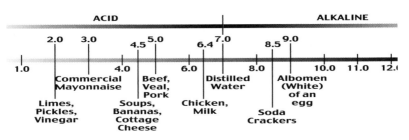

III. Temperature

Microorganisms thrive in warmth. Temperatures between 4°C (40°F) and 60°C (140°F) (called the "temperature danger zone") are the range in which they grow and multiply the best.

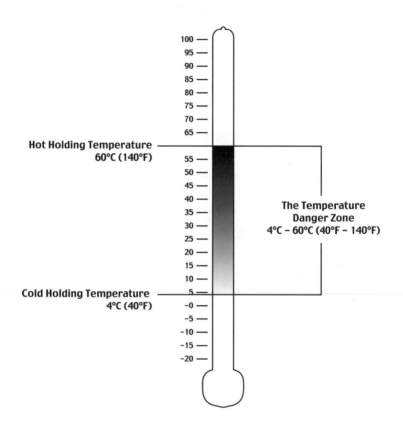

Most bacteria are killed if exposed to temperatures above 60°C (140°F) for several minutes. They are **not** killed when they are refrigerated or frozen; they merely become dormant. Some bacteria, like *Listeria monocytogenes* actually grow well at refrigeration temperatures. Some bacteria produce spores (hard shells that protect the microorganism) that can often survive extreme heat and cold.

Key Points of Control
- Keep hot foods hot (60° C/140° F or higher) and cold foods cold (4° C/40° F) to prevent growth of microorganisms.
- Use up older refrigerated foods before newer foods in order to prevent growing numbers of "cold loving" bacteria like *Listeria monocytogenes.*

2

IV. Time

Microorganisms need time to grow to a stage where they can do us harm. If bacteria have the right conditions, they can double every 10 to 20 minutes. Pathogenic bacteria such as Salmonella spp. may cause illness with as few as four or five cells. In this case, temperature abuse of one hour may be too much. In most cases, temperature abuse of a product for two to four hours may lead to food poisoning. Temperature abuse is cumulative. Therefore, a product might be abused at shipping, receiving, in storage and during preparation. Although the temperature abuse may be for only 30 minutes at each step, the total or cumulative time may be two hours or more producing enough microorganisms to make someone ill.

How Bacteria Reproduce

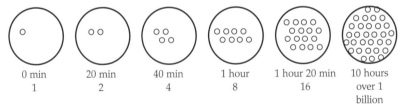

0 min	20 min	40 min	1 hour	1 hour 20 min	10 hours
1	2	4	8	16	over 1 billion

At room temperature, one bacteria can multiply
to unsafe numbers in just over two hours.

Key Points of Control

- Microorganisms need sufficient time to grow. It is very important not to give bacteria a "time opportunity" to grow.
- Practice good and timely handling and storage procedures throughout the flow of food to decrease the time food remains in the temperature danger zone.

V. Oxygen

Most pathogenic bacteria need oxygen to live. Therefore, some products can be preserved by vacuum packaging (where all the air has been removed), or gas flushing (where the air has been removed and replaced with a mixture of carbon dioxide and nitrogen). Prepackaged deli meats are often vacuum-packed. Fresh pasta is often gas flushed to prevent the growth of pathogenic and spoilage bacteria.

On the other hand, a few pathogenic bacteria prefer the absence of oxygen. The growth of *Clostridium botulinum* can occur in canned foods or some gas flushed packages. This pathogen can produce a neurotoxin in the food that can cause illness and possibly death. This organism will not grow at refrigeration temperatures.

Key Points of Control

- Do not open vacuum packaged or gas flushed products until you are ready to use them. This helps to preserve them.
- Vacuum packaged and gas flushed products should always be kept refrigerated (or stored as per the label instructions) to prevent the growth of *Clostridium botulinum*.
- Do not use canned products that are bulging or blown from gas production inside the can.

VI. Moisture

Microorganisms need moisture to grow. Foods such as fresh meat and poultry, dairy products and many fruits and vegetables have high levels of available moisture for growth of microorganisms. Dry foods such as powdered ingredients keep longer because of their low moisture content. Adding salt or sugar to bind the available water preserves some foods. Jams and jellies are examples of products that are high in water content, and are preserved through high sugar levels. Microorganisms can survive in dried products, but are unlikely to grow. Milk powder is one dried food that can support the survival of bacteria.

For a list of common bacterial pathogens, their sources and symptoms of their illness see Appendix H - Major Foodborne Illnesses.

Key Points of Control

- Keep dry ingredients dry when not in use. Adding water will allow the growth of microorganisms.
- Keep equipment, utensils, serviceware, pots, pans and other food contact surfaces dry when not in use.
- Don't allow pooling water on floors, tables or other places in the establishment, as bacteria and mould will grow and possibly contaminate the food at a later date.

2

2. Physical Hazards

Physical hazards include things in food that can cause choking or internal injury to customers. They are any foreign material present in the food product or menu that are not a part of the recipe.

Material	Sources
Glass	Light bulbs and fixtures, unprotected windows, jars, drinking glasses, eye glasses, bottles, plates and gauge covers.
Wood	Fields, boxes, buildings, pallets.
Stones	Fields, buildings.
Metal	Machinery, equipment, fields, wire, needles in meat products, employee jewelry and staples in boxes (metal).
Bone	Fish, improper processing at plants.
Plastic	Ingredient bags, gloves, contact lenses, and aprons.

Foodservice operators should always be watching for possible physical hazards that could contaminate the product. Prevention and detection of physical hazards should be addressed as part of your HACCP plan.

3. Chemical Hazards

Food can become contaminated with chemicals before or after it arrives at a foodservice operation. These hazards include:

Type of Chemical Hazard	Examples	Preventative Measure
Agricultural Chemicals	Pesticides, antibiotics, herbicides, fertilizers.	• Ask suppliers to demonstrate that programs are in place to prevent the contamination of the product with these chemicals. • Ask to see Certificates of Analysis. • Choose HACCP recognized suppliers.
Industrial Chemicals	Cleaners and sanitizers, non-food grade lubricants on equipment, ammonia from refrigeration units.	• Keep cleaners and sanitizers and other chemicals away from food. • Use food grade lubricants. • Use proper cleaning and rinsing procedure. • Choose HACCP recognized suppliers.

Type of Chemical Hazard	Examples	Preventative Measure
Naturally Occurring Toxins	Aflatoxins or vomotoxins in flour or other cereal products produced by moulds.	• Ask suppliers to demonstrate that programs are in place to prevent the contamination of the product with these chemicals. • Ask to see Certificates of Analysis.
Food Chemicals	Preservatives such as sulphites	• Use only as directed. • See 4. Allergens for allergen management procedure. • Choose HACCP recognized suppliers.

4. Allergens

Customers can sometimes have adverse reactions to food. Some of these reactions cause a range of discomfort and others can cause death. From a food safety perspective, foodservice operators are most concerned about food allergies and anaphylaxis, which can be life threatening.

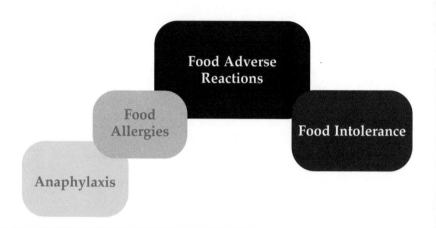

Examples:

Food Intolerance: Lactose intolerance, which includes the inability to digest dairy products. Consumers can also have intolerant reactions to sulphite that is present in glazed fruits, grapes, candy bars etc.

Food Allergies: Reaction to food protein such as egg whites. Wheat and other gluten products cause allergic reactions. Food allergies may affect only certain organs of the body.

Anaphylaxis: Reaction to food protein. Peanuts, peanut products, and shellfish can cause extremely serious anaphylactic reactions. Can affect all organs in the body. In the most severe cases, symptoms such as respiratory failure, coma and/or heart failure can occur.

The most serious food allergies are caused by:

- Peanuts
- Tree nuts (including almonds, brazil nuts, cashews, macadamias, pecans, pine nuts, pistachios, and walnuts)
- Sesame seeds
- Milk and milk components such as casein
- Eggs and products containing egg whites
- Fish and shellfish (including clams, crab, crayfish, lobster, mussels, oysters, prawns, scallops, and shrimp)
- Soy and products containing soy protein
- Wheat and products containing wheat protein
- Sulphites

These ingredients can cause serious illness and sometimes death in hypersensitive people.

Key Points of Control

- Understand which menu items contain allergens and communicate this to customers.
- Train employees to understand food allergies and how to minimize cross-contamination between menu items that contain allergens and menu items that do not.
- Wash food contact surfaces, utensils, pots, pans and service ware thoroughly to minimize cross contamination.
- Do not mix even small amounts of foods containing allergens with foods that do not contain allergens unless customers are told the mixed food contains allergens.

Section III
Construction, Design,
and Facilities

III - Construction, Design, and Facilities

1. Building Construction & Facility Design

MD

1.1. A Foodservice building must be constructed and located to meet:
- Local building ordinances
- Public health regulations
- Fire and safety regulations
- Approved construction standards for use of the area

The construction and location of an establishment is important in providing a barrier against surrounding environmental hazards/contaminants. Selecting the building construction materials specifically designed for commercial food premise use can reduce the chance of contamination.

- When choosing a site for a foodservice operation, it is important that the site is free from any hazardous conditions. For example, surrounding conditions that can lead to contamination include dust, foul odours, smoke, pest infestation and airborne hazards. It is important that the site is set apart from potential sources of contamination or offensive/hazardous industry such as waste disposal facilities.
- If you plan on construction or alterations/renovations, be sure to consult the local regulatory authority. Many jurisdictions require plans for new construction, alterations and extensive remodeling to be approved by the local Health Department or regulatory agency.
- The design and layout of facilities such as the kitchen, dishwashing and dining areas should provide a safe food environment in which work can be done effectively. Ensure the materials selected are suitable for the intended purpose of the area. For example floors, walls and ceiling must be constructed of a material that is easily cleaned and maintained in an effort to contribute to a safe food environment.
- In a foodservice environment there is excess moisture, temperature fluctuations and constant traffic flow. For this reason all facility materials must be resistant to these

extreme conditions and possible damage. If necessary, consult an expert in the area of commercial materials and/or products available for the foodservice industry.

- Once pests have infested a facility, it can be very difficult to eliminate them. Pest infestation leads to the spread of disease, and damage to food, supplies and facilities. The building facility must be constructed and maintained in a way to prevent the entrance of insects and rodents.

- Equipment should be located within the facility to allow for safe access during use and to be easily accessible from all sides. The equipment and utensils should be designed and constructed to be durable under normal use and conditions.

- Foodservice equipment and utensils should comply with international sanitation standards such as NSF International (NSFI), Underwriters' Laboratories of Canada (ULC) and Canadian Standards Association (CSA). (See Equipment and Utensil Section V)

HR

1.2. Facility layout should be designed in one direction following the flow of food. Non-food preparation areas (i.e. dishwashing area) should be reasonably separated from the food preparation areas.

The design of the establishment is important in preventing cross-contamination between the different activities involved in food preparation. For example, if unsanitary operations are conducted close to sanitary operations, the risk of contamination is increased.

- The design should follow the flow of food in one direction, from receiving, to storage, to preparation, to serving or packaging/serving. When the establishment is not set up to follow this flow-of-food production, then the establishment should arrange food preparation areas/tasks to avoid cross-contamination. First develop a diagram of the flow-of-food and identify areas of potential cross-contamination. Then re-arrange these potential unsafe food preparation tasks to eliminate the cross-contamination. For example, if food handlers are currently required to walk through the dishwashing area with raw or finished food products, simply create a new route for the food handlers to avoid the contact with the dishwashing area and any potential cross-contamination.

- There should be an area for handling, storing, cleaning, and preparing of raw food ingredients. This area should be separate from the cooked, ready-to-eat food display, handling, and serving areas.
- Non-food preparation areas or activities, for example cleaning supplies and chemical storage areas, should be separated from food preparation areas. To minimize the opportunity for food to become contaminated, all cleaning supplies and chemicals should be stored in a separate, locked, dry and well-lit area.

2. Walls & Ceilings

MD

2.1. Wall surfaces in the food preparation, storage and ware-washing area (i.e. dish/pot washing area) must be constructed of materials that resist the growth of microorganisms and allow for continuous washing.

If the walls and surrounding areas cannot withstand the food premise environment (i.e. excess moisture and steam, constant washing, cleaning and scrubbing), then this could result in contamination of the food product. Peeling, flaking or chipped paint from walls could pose a physical hazard by contaminating the food product. If the walls are cracked and/or porous, this could result in ineffective cleaning and a place where bacteria can grow.

- Wall surfaces should be constructed of hard, smooth, non-absorbent, light coloured materials, which are easily cleaned. Such materials include tile, plaster, sealed brick and stainless steel.
- All wall and ceiling joints should be tight and sealed.

3. Floors

MD

3.1. Floors in food preparation and processing/equipment areas (i.e. dish/utensil wash, walk-in refrigerators, freezers, toilet and dressing rooms) must be of smooth, slip-resistant, non-absorptive and non-flaking or peeling material. Floors that are subject to moisture must be constructed of non-porous materials.

3

It is important that the floor does not absorb moisture and is resistant to microbial growth or mould. A floor that easily deteriorates could be a source of contamination during preparation of the food.

• In a foodservice operation, floor surfaces should be resistant to damage and deterioration from water/moisture, cleaning agents and repeated contact and scrubbing.

• Materials that are smooth, non-slip, durable, easily cleaned and normally resistant to acids, alkalis, grease or other organic matter should be used for floors in these areas. Additionally, floors should be sufficiently hard to resist cracking, denting, heaving, or buckling from equipment weight or the action of mobile equipment. Examples of these materials include quarry tile and terrazzo.

MD

3.2. Floor design must be sloped to allow for draining of liquids. Floor drains must meet all plumbing codes. Cross connections between potable and non-potable water and waste lines are not permitted. If cross connections are discovered, immediate action must be taken to ensure the safety of food.

Floors that are constructed with slopes will allow draining and avoid the pooling of liquids. This will minimize unsanitary conditions and decrease the risk of contamination. Drains and drain lines can eliminate the accumulation of liquids. The separation of floor drains from sewage drains prevents the contamination of floor drains with human waste and other sewage.

- In the foodservice operation, sloped floors are needed to reduce pooling liquids and to drain water where water-flush methods are used for cleaning. The floor must be sloped a minimum of 2% to a drain to allow for water drainage. If there are water pools, make sure to remove by mopping the area at a frequency that will eliminate any standing water and the growth of microorganisms.

- It is recommended that the flooring surface material be carried up the wall for a distance of at least 15 cm (6 inches). If there is a joint between floor and wall, it should be sealed or coved (coving is a curved or sealed edge between the floor and wall that eliminates sharp corners or gaps) to eliminate water penetration. This is necessary to prevent pests from entering and living in the facility, as well as to allow effective cleaning and sanitation. This will reduce the growth of microorganisms such as mould.

- The floor drains are to be located so they can be accessed and cleaned on a regular basis to promote effective draining of liquids and eliminate flooding. Drain lines are to be individually trapped and vented to the outside. All drainage systems should be constructed so there are no cross connections. A cross connection is any physical link between drains, sewers or waste pipes and water that is considered to be safe-to-drink (potable) water supply.

HR

3.3. Carpeting should be laid over firm, sealed under-flooring, and only where permitted. Carpet should be cleaned, in good repair, and of a material that can be cleaned by proper cleaning methods.

Sanitary flooring will allow for easier cleaning and decrease the risk of microbial growth contamination of the food.

- Carpeting is difficult to clean, absorbs water and can harbour bacteria, odours, dust and other contaminants. Food operation areas may not use carpeting. If there is carpet, it should only be used in the dining or public areas.

A Case in Point

A quick service restaurant is remodeling their kitchen area. Although the equipment in the facility is not new, it still meets current design and construction standards. However, the floors and walls in the restaurant are old and need to be upgraded. The owner/operator is considering using unfinished pinewood to replace the flooring.

The Problem:
Wood is porous and absorbs water and other liquids. This type of flooring would not be durable and easy to clean. Floors and walls should be non-absorbent, easily cleanable, durable and smooth. Walls should be light in colour and also easy to clean.

Solution:
The owner/operator should contact the local regulatory agency and review the remodeling plans and materials before installation. This will verify that they meet current code requirements and regulations. This verification process should be documented in writing, signed and dated by the appropriate regulatory authority.

3

4. Stairs, Catwalks and Mezzanines

MD

4.1. Stairways should be located so as to minimize the risk of food contamination and constructed of materials that are slip resistant and easily cleanable.

Stairs, catwalks and mezzanines, if located over food preparation areas, can be a source of contamination.

• In the foodservice operation, stairs, catwalks or mezzanines should not be located over food preparation areas. This is necessary to avoid any contamination such as physical hazards falling into the food product below.
• Stairs, catwalks and mezzanines should be accessible and easily cleaned. This is necessary to decrease the risk of contamination.

- Catwalks and mezzanines should be constructed of solid masonry or metal construction with raised edges to prevent contamination from falling onto areas below.

5. Utilities: Lighting

MD

5.1. Lighting and lighting fixtures must be designed to prevent accumulation of dirt and be easily cleanable.

The accumulation or dust, dirt and insects in light bulb fixtures is not only unappealing to look at, but it is a sign of untimely maintenance and cleaning. Dust and debris on lighting can cause microbial pathogens. If this debris is excessive, it can fall into the food below and can cause foodborne illness in customers.

- Lighting in a foodservice operation can accumulate dust, dirt, bacteria and other contaminants. Therefore, it is necessary to clean the lighting on a regular basis to avoid contamination of the food contact surfaces and food products below.

MD

5.2. Light bulbs must be shielded or shatterproof to protect food and food contact surfaces from broken glass.

Light bulbs must be covered or shatterproof to prevent glass fragments (a physical hazard) from contaminating food and food contact surfaces. Broken glass from light fixtures can cause serious illness and injury to customers.

- Light bulbs need to be shielded or have a protective shatterproof coating. This is necessary particularly for lights installed in canopies and located above food preparation work surfaces and equipment. In these areas, there may be exposed food, equipment, utensils, linens or unwrapped single-service and single-use articles that could easily be contaminated.
- If a foodservice operation uses infra-red or other heat lamps, they must be protected against breakage. A shield surrounding and extending beyond the bulb so that only the face of the bulb is exposed is necessary to prevent the glass fragments from contaminating the food or food contact surface, in the case of breakage.

MD

5.3. Food premises must be supplied with sufficient artificial light to ensure the safe and sanitary production of food.

Sufficient lighting is a very important feature of a foodservice operation. It promotes sanitary conditions by identifying unclean areas. Lighting is essential in a food operation to clearly reveal all cleaning requirements, insect or rodent infestations and to meet safety requirements.

In a foodservice operation there are different light intensities recommended depending on the type of work that is to be done. Lighting should be located directly over dishwashing and food preparation work areas.

The FRFS Code recommends the following intensities. Light intensities of 110 lux be provided in:
- Walk-in coolers;
- Dry food storage; and
- In all other areas and rooms during periods of cleaning.

Light intensities of 220 lux be provided in:
- The area where fresh produce or packaged foods are sold;
- The handwashing area;
- The dishwashing and wearwashing areas;
- The equipment storage;
- The utensil storage; and
- The toilet rooms.

It is recommended that light intensities of 540 lux be provided in food preparation areas:
- Where potentially hazardous food are handled;
- Where food utensils and equipment such as knives, slicers, grinders or saws are used; and
- Where employee/worker safety is a factor.

Lux is a unit of illumination. A foot-candle illuminates one foot around its diameter. 10 lux represents the light produced by a foot-candle.

6. Utilities: Ventilation

MD

6.1. Ventilation systems must conform to National Building Codes, Public Health and Fire Regulations, and be specifically designed to avoid back-drips of contaminating material into food, food contact equipment or surfaces, utensils, linens, and/or single-service and single-use articles from vents or hoods.

In the foodservice operation there are odours, gases and air-borne dirt and mould that can cause contamination. It is necessary for a ventilation system to remove this contamination and supply air of good quality.

- The standard ventilation systems used in a foodservice operation consist of a hood, fan, intake and exhaust air ducts and vents. The capacity of the ventilation system should be based on the quantity of vapour and hot air to be removed. Refer to the National Building Code for Regulations. (See Appendix I – Helpful Contact Information).
- Noxious fumes are never to be vented into public areas unless suitably treated to avoid creating a nuisance or a health hazard.
- Air intakes should be designed to prevent the entrance of dust, dirt, insects, rodents or any other contaminating materials, and located to prevent direct air across or on food preparation surfaces or food. This means that they should be louvered and/or screened. Air filters may also be used on air intakes.

MD

6.2. Mechanical ventilation systems must meet and be cleaned in accordance with frequencies stipulated in local regulations.

Keeping the ventilation system free of grease and dust accumulation will prevent contamination and a potential fire hazard.

- Ventilation systems become a sanitation hazard when dirt

build-up falls on food items below.

- Many fires in foodservice operations are caused by grease accumulation in filters and ducts. The filters or other grease-extracting equipment must be designed for easy removal for cleaning and/or replacement.
- Filters should be cleaned or replaced at regular intervals. Also, they should be cleaned in accordance with frequencies stipulated in local Fire Regulations and/or Building Codes.

7. Utilities: Plumbing

MD

7.1. All plumbing systems must be:
- Of a size and material in accordance with local Plumbing Code regulations;
- Installed and maintained in accordance with local Plumbing Code regulations; and
- Approved by the local or provincial/territorial building authorities.

MD

7.2. Potable (safe-to-drink) water lines, food product lines or equipment must be separate from, and installed in such a manner as to prevent any cross-connection with, or contamination from sewage, non-potable water or liquid waste lines.

The plumbing system is extremely important to food safety. The plumbing system in a foodservice operation carries both the potable (safe-to-drink) water essential to safe foodservice and sanitation procedures, as well as sewage wastes (non-potable water) which are a possible source of dangerous food contamination. Therefore the design of the plumbing system, below the floor and as exposed overhead lines, could be a potential source of food and food contact surface contamination. Contamination of the public water supply in a food establishment is a real public health risk. Outbreaks of dysentery, typhoid fever and chemical poisonings have been traced to cross-connections (i.e. any physical link through which contaminants from drains, sewers or waste pipes can enter a potable (safe-to-drink) water supply and other types of plumbing hazards in a foodservice operation.

- The plumbing system must be installed to eliminate back-flow, back-syphonage and cross-connections. For example, one of the most common cross connections in the foodservice industry is a garden hose attached to a janitor's service sink with the end of the hose submerged in a pail of soapy water that is used to clean the floors. Suction in the water lines could siphon the water from the pail into the potable (safe-to-drink) water system and contaminate it. This could result in serving unclean water to customers.
- Back-flow prevention devices – such as air gaps, vacuum breakers that prevent back-flows, should be installed in compliance with the local Plumbing and Building Codes.
- The foodservice operation's plumbing system must be properly maintained (i.e. no drips/leakage) so access for maintenance or emergency situations can be made, and all piping should be designed to be large enough to handle the required volume of water and sewage.
- It is important to have licensed plumbers install and maintain the plumbing systems. For example, plumbing lines should be installed within permanent walls, ceilings, or floors. It is necessary to have clearly identified potable and non-potable water lines.
- Plumbing lines should not be above food preparation areas or above food storage and there should never be exposed overhead plumbing lines. This could be a source of contamination to the food contact surfaces and food products below.

Note: If there is human waste (faecal contamination) in the potable drain line, the foodservice operator is at a very serious risk of harming the public. If this happens, the facility must immediately discontinue the use of the water system for all food preparation, cooking, servicing and cleaning. Another source of potable (safe-to-drink) water must be found and the problem with the cross-connection fixed by a professional plumber before resuming the use of the system.

8. Utilities: Water and Steam Supply

MD

8.1. Potable (safe-to-drink) water must be provided from public or private sources approved by the local or provincial/territorial regulatory agency.

The water supply used for human consumption, cleaning, cooking, and washing of produce and dishes must be of a safe and sanitary quality in order to avoid contamination of food equipment, food, and customer waterborne illness. Unsafe water can carry bacteria, viruses and parasites.

- Water provided in a foodservice operation must be potable (safe-to-drink) if it is for human consumption.
- It is the responsibility of the operator to have new or temporary water supplies approved before use. For example, water from a private well (a source not subject to routine bacteriological examination) must be checked on a regular basis and be of a quality acceptable to the local authorities.
- A foodservice operation equipped with its own private water supply should have a written water sampling plan and protocol. Samples of the water should be tested at a government or accredited laboratory monthly or at a frequency deemed necessary by the regulatory agency. Test results for potable (safe-to-drink) water in most jurisdictions must meet or exceed the minimum health requirements as prescribed in the current publication of the Guidelines for Canadian Drinking Water Quality, published by Health Canada.
- In foodservice operations where water cannot be piped into an establishment (i.e. a mobile vendor), it can be transported and held in approved (by local health authorities) sanitary containers and must be dispensed in a clean and sanitary manner. It is important to use only approved containers because chemicals can leach out of containers not approved for water or food use.

Use of non-potable water:

Non-potable (NOT safe-to-drink) water is only permitted for use in air conditioning or fire protection. It must be completely separate (and labelled) from potable water. Non-potable water must never come into contact directly or indirectly with food, food contact surfaces, food equipment or handwashing facilities.

Water Emergencies:

Occasionally, an emergency may disrupt the water supply. If a foodservice operation is informed of the presence of contaminated water and the establishment decides to remain in operation, the following steps must be taken to ensure potable (safe-to-drink) water is available:

Step 1 – Use bottled water or thoroughly boiled water (rapid, rolling boil of the water for at least five minutes prior to use) for beverages, food washing and ingredients in food recipes.

Step 2 – Use commercially prepared ice or make ice only from boiled water.

Step 3 - Use boiled water for essential cleaning such as food contact surfaces. Consider using single-use plates and utensils to minimize washing requirements.

Step 4 – Have a supply of warm (previously boiled) water for handwashing.

(See Appendix B - Boil Water Advisory)

MD

8.2. Hot and cold water under pressure, and in sufficient quantities must be provided to meet the peak demands throughout the food premises, and be provided in all areas where food is prepared or equipment and utensils washed.

For cleaning and sanitizing to be effective, hot water must be at a temperature hot enough to reduce the level of harmful microorganisms to minimize health risks.

• The optimum temperature for cleaning depends on the method and chemicals used. For instance, manual dishwashing requires a temperature of no less than 45°C (113°F) and mechanical dishwashing may be as high as 60°C (140°F). See Section VI – Cleaning and Sanitation.

- Check pressure and temperature of water during high peak hours of operation. Check the water temperature daily with a calibrated thermometer to verify that it reaches expected temperature.

MD

8.3. Steam supplies, where used directly on food, food contact surfaces and as a food ingredient, must be clean (potable water) and non-toxic and tested regularly.

The steam supply used for human consumption must be of a safe and sanitary quality in order to avoid contamination of food equipment or food. Unsafe steam can carry bacterial spores, viruses, parasites, and toxic chemicals.

- The steam supplied to cooking equipment such as cappuccino makers and steamers must be free from chemicals and microorganisms. For example, when a customer receives a cappuccino, steam is an actual ingredient and if it is not safe this could act as a health hazard. Water used to generate steam must be potable (safe-to-drink) and be free of cleaning chemicals or other chemical contaminants.

9. Utilities: Sewage

MD

9.1. Sewage must be disposed of in an approved public sewage system or in a manner approved by public health authorities to prevent contamination of food and/or water supplies.

Sewage and waste water may carry pathogenic bacteria, viruses and parasites, and/or chemicals harmful to the public. Foodservice operations must dispose of sewage and waste in a manner that does not contaminate the product.

- A backup of raw sewage is cause for immediate closure of any foodservice operation. There must be immediate corrective action taken for the problem and a thorough cleaning of the entire operation should be done after the problem is corrected.

- Health authorities must approve the installation and location of individual sewage disposal systems in a foodservice operation. This confirms there are no cross-connections leading to contamination of the potable water supply.
- Sewage waste systems and other non-sewage liquid conveyance and disposal systems should be flushed clean on a periodic basis. This will ensure proper maintenance and cleanliness of the system so as to avoid contamination.

10. Food Waste and Garbage

10.1. Food waste and garbage must be handled, maintained, stored, and removed from the premises in a way that will prevent food contamination or pest infestation.

Food waste and garbage are a source of food contamination, odours, insects, and rodents. Operators must have a routine waste removal program in place. Proper disposal and storage of food waste and garbage will reduce the chance of microbial cross-contamination through pest control, movement of equipment products, and personnel.

Indoor Solid Waste Containers

It is recommended that solid waste containers within the foodservice operation be:
- Made of leak-proof, non-absorptive, easily cleaned containers with tight-fitting covers;
- Designed to minimize both the attraction of pests and the potential for airborne contamination;
- In sufficient number and accessible;
- Emptied when full or at least daily;
- Identified as to their contents such as waste, refuse, recyclable materials; and
- Be cleaned on a regular basis.

Outdoor Solid Waste Containers

Solid waste containers located outside the premises should be:
- Maintained so as not to attract pests, since dirty containers attract pest and rodents;
- Equipped with covers and closed when not in use; and
- Cleaned on a regular basis and emptied when full or at least two times per week.

MD

10.2. Garbage storage rooms and containers must be emptied, cleaned and sanitized as often as necessary. This should be done as part of routine maintenance and at least weekly.

Garbage storage rooms and containers can become a breeding ground for pests and microorganisms. These areas are very susceptible to the rapid growth of harmful microorganisms because they are usually moist, warm and provide a source of food. Pests are also attracted to these areas because of the ready source of food. If the garbage storage rooms and containers are regularly emptied, cleaned and sanitized, the number of pests and microorganisms will be minimized.

Cleaning of Waste Containers

Garbage/solid waste containers should be:
- Cleaned and sanitized after each use, inside and outside;
- Manually cleaned with a hand scrub brush and detergent and water and followed by a sanitation rinse;
- Mechanically, cleaned with a steam pressure hose or car-washing equipment; and
- Cleaned in an area separate from food preparation, storage and service.

Note: Waste water produced while cleaning containers is considered sewage and must be disposed of in a sanitary manner.

11. Handwash Stations

MD

11.1. At least one handwash station, designed to comply with the provisions of the National Building Code enforced by the local regulatory authority, must be conveniently accessible to all staffing food preparation areas.

Food handler's hands are the primary source of contamination of food products in a foodservice operation. Conveniently located and fully equipped handwashing facilities are key factors in getting employees to routinely wash their hands to minimize this contamination.

- In a foodservice operation, the number of handwashing stations required and the location of these stations are governed by the National Building Code.
- A handwashing station must be conveniently located for use by food handlers in the food preparation area. It must be accessible to workers at all times.
- Handwashing stations must be located both where workers are serving food and handling money. Employees are expected to wash their hands frequently to minimize contamination to food products.
- It is important that handwashing facilities never be used for purposes other than handwashing. For example, produce preparation and warewashing must never be done in handwash sinks. Dedicating sinks for handwash purposes only, ensures that they are clean and free from gross contamination.

All employee handwashing facilities must be equipped with:

a) Single-use liquid soap dispensers and single-use hand drying devices such as paper hand towel dispensers, or properly functioning cloth roll dispensers;

b) Hot and cold, or pre-mixed warm, running water;

c) An adequate flow of water. If a self-closing faucet is installed, it should flow for at least 20 seconds, without the need to reactivate the faucet;

d) A handwashing sign posted which explains the proper hand washing procedures to staff; and

e) Equipment that is easily cleanable, and maintained in a clean and sanitary condition.

A Case In Point

In a small restaurant that specialized in pizza and wings, a prep cook was diagnosed with Hepatitis A. As a result, several employees and customers were required to be immunized against the disease. An inspection by the Health Department revealed that the handwashing station in the food preparation area was out of service. The only other handwashing stations available to employees on duty were those located in the restrooms. The lack of a properly operating handwashing station in the kitchen caused the cross-contamination from the prep cook to the other workers and customers.

The Problem:
When food workers cannot conveniently wash their contaminated hands, the risk of food contamination and cross-contamination is high. Many employees will not take the time to walk to a restroom, but rather wipe their hands on a towel or their apron. It is extremely important to take the time to wash hands as soon as they become contaminated.

Solution:
The restaurant operator should have repaired the handwash sink immediately. The infected worker should not have worked until a physician certified him/her to be free of the Hepatitis A virus. The restaurant is likely to get a reputation as a result of this outbreak, and the long-term implications might result in financial ruin.

What should you do if not enough handwash stations are available?
If approved by the regulatory authority and when food handling or food exposure is limited, alternative handwashing facilities may be used. These include shared handwashing facilities in conjunction with other plumbed services such as dishwashing sinks, hand sanitizing dips, and/or alcohol based hand cleansers.

12. Restroom Facilities

MD

12.1. Restroom requirements are set by the National Building Code and are regulated by local agencies. Toilet facilities are required for all employees in sufficient numbers and must be equipped in accordance with the regulatory agency.

Toilet facilities should be properly located to minimize food contamination from faecal matter. Foodservice operations that are kept clean, in good repair and properly equipped will minimize the spread of faecal matter and other contamination that may be caused by pests, humans, and equipment.

Foodservice operations should have separate restroom facilities for customers and employees. All restroom facilities should:

- Be completely enclosed and provided with a tight-fitting and self-closing door;
- Be equipped with handwashing facilities within or immediately nearby to toilet facilities;
- Be equipped with an adequate flow of water, hot and cold or pre-mixed warm; liquid soap; and single-use hand-drying devices such as paper hand towels, or roll dispensers;
- Be equipped with handwashing signs prominently displayed;
- Be conveniently located and accessible to workers during all hours of operation;
- Provide hooks outside the toilet enclosure to hang aprons, white coats, etc;
- Be easily cleanable, well ventilated, and well lit;
- Not open directly into a food preparation or food storage area; and
- Be equipped with a garbage can for disposable paper towels.

13. Dressing Areas

13.1. Dressing areas should be provided if workers routinely change their clothes in the food premises.

Separate dressing rooms can minimize the wearing of street clothes in food preparation areas. Dressing rooms can also promote the practice of having dedicated clean and sanitary work uniforms. Uniform changes that do not take place at the foodservice operation can result in contamination of these clothes at home, during transit to work, and during other non-work related occasions. This risk can be minimized through the use of dressing rooms.

If the foodservice operation has a separate dressing area, it should be:

- Easily cleanable;
- Well ventilated and lit;
- Provided with lockers or other suitable facilities for the storage of workers' possessions;
- Completely enclosed and provided with a lockable door, unless separate facilities are provided for each sex; and
- Located separate from food storage, handling, and preparation or serving areas.

14. Janitorial Facilities

MD

14.1. All food premises must be equipped with cleaning materials, equipment and facilities.

Dirty water from wet floor cleaning is a source of contamination as it contains microbiological and chemical contaminants. It is necessary to have a service sink or curbed cleaning facility with a drain. This will allow for the safe disposal of waste water. Cleaning utensils such as mops, brushes and pails should have a designated storage area when not in use to decrease risk of contamination to food and food contact surfaces

In a foodservice operation, a janitorial facility should:

- Be located away from food handling areas;
- Be equipped with a service sink or curbed cleaning facility to dispose of waste water;
- Be equipped with a floor drain, which is conveniently located for the cleaning of mops or similar wet floor cleaning tools, and for the disposal of mop water and similar

liquid waste; and
- Have a facility to store brooms, mops, pails, and cleaning compounds when not in use.

15. Storage Areas

MD

15.1. Foodservice operations must have storage facilities for food, food ingredients, equipment, and non-food materials such as utensils, linens, single-service and single-use articles, packaging, and chemical agents. They need to be maintained in a manner that protects food and food contact services from contamination. All food items must be stored in a separate location away from non-food items including packaging materials.

Contamination of food, food ingredients and equipment can occur in unsanitary storage facilities. Separation of storages for food, food contact surfaces and non-food material reduces the risks of cross contamination.

During storage, food and food contact surfaces must be protected from contamination such as dust, dirt, water, pest infestation and any other unsanitary condition such as raw meat dripping on ready-to-eat food.

The sanitary and mechanical condition of storage areas should help to maximize the potential shelf life of products and protect food from contamination.

Storage areas should never be located:

- In areas used for the storage of soiled linens;
- In locker rooms;
- In toilet rooms;
- In garbage rooms;
- In mechanical rooms;
- Under sewer lines that are not shielded to intercept potential drips; and
- In the same room or in the vicinity of chemicals or pesticides.

Organize the storage room/area with:

- Adequate shelving for supplies.
- Shelving, if not sealed to the floor, raised off the floor at least 15 cm (6 inches);
- Shelving at least 5 cm (2 inches) from the walls to allow for access and permit easier visual inspection for pests and dirt;
- If shelving is attached to the wall, ensure that it is easily accessible for cleaning and storage purposes; and
- Food and food items a minimum of 15 cm (6 inches) off the floor to permit cleaning and minimize pest access.

Non-food storage

- Store non-food products such as linens, packaging, and single service utensils/containers in an area that prevents the potential for contamination with food, food ingredients, equipment and non-food materials such as chemicals. Other non-food materials such as landscaping tools, marketing materials and posters must also be stored in a manner so as to minimize contamination of food.
- Store personal belongings of employees separately from food storage and food preparation areas.

Recyclables

In foodservice operations, all recyclables such as bottles and cans need to be stored in a sanitary manner and removed regularly to prevent the harborage and infestation of pests. For example, if pop cans are not rinsed and stored in a sanitary manner, they can attract insects into the premise, creating unsanitary conditions.

Section IV
Control of Hazards
Following the Flow
of Food

IV. Control of Hazards Following the Flow of Food

1. Purchasing & Approved Suppliers

1.1. All food and food ingredients received at a food premises must be obtained from sources approved by the regulatory authority having jurisdiction.

The flow of food begins with purchasing. Safe food begins with reliable suppliers who currently meet inspection standards of the jurisdiction's regulatory authority and/or operate in a manner that prevents and controls contamination of food. Effective purchasing paves the way for a successful and safe foodservice operation. Purchasing is a highly skilled activity requiring knowledge of products and current market conditions. Purchasing from approved suppliers will give an operator confidence that the purchased food is both safe and wholesome

What to look for when choosing a supplier.

The company should:

- Be reliable;
- Use properly refrigerated delivery trucks when required;
- Train their employees in food safety and sanitation;
- Use clean, protective, leak-proof, sturdy packaging
- Adjust delivery schedules so that deliveries arrive during off-peak hours;
- Cooperate with your employees inspecting the food when it is delivered; and
- Allow you to inspect their delivery trucks and production facilities for any evidence of potential contamination (i.e. dirty delivery trucks, signs of pests) or factors that could lead to potential contamination.

Approved Sources

All of the following must be purchased from approved suppliers:

- Potentially hazardous food and food ingredients such as meat, poultry, fish, eggs and milk, and other foods capable of supporting the growth of pathogenic microorganisms;
- Foods in hermetically sealed containers and/or products packaged under modified atmosphere packaging; and
- Game animals from commercial game farms that raise, slaughter and process the animals as per the regulatory authority having jurisdiction.

Note: Government-inspected and/or graded foods should have the appropriate stamp indicating such inspection and/or grading has been carried out.

Unapproved Sources

Food prepared in a private home or any other place, which is not approved by the regulatory agency having jurisdiction must not be used or offered for human consumption in a food premise. This also applies to wild game that has not been inspected and approved by the jurisdiction's regulatory authority. In some jurisdictions, regulatory authorities may allow some exemptions to this requirement. Check with your local regulatory authority.

2. Inspection and Receiving

MD

2.1. All food products received at a food premise must be properly packaged and labelled, according to requirements outlined in the Food and Drugs Act and Regulation, and the Consumer Packaging and Labelling Act and Regulations.

To ensure that products received by the foodservice operation are traceable and legal under federal law, products must be properly labelled. In the event of a recall, lot coding is essential, as it allows tracing and recall of products.

It is important that the receiver carefully inspect deliveries for proper labeling. Do not accept any products that have lost their original labels. For example, if you receive canned products without labels, it is impossible to determine the contents, identify lot code and verify if the product contains any allergens. This is a severe health risk for the customer. If product is unlabelled (such as carcasses, produce, bakery products or split lots), invoices, receipts, and lot coding information must be retained, to allow tracking of these unlabelled products

Keep all seafood tags for a minimum of 90 days after use.

2.2. All food and food ingredients received at food premises must be visually inspected for acceptability, as they are received.

Accepting safe food products is a critical part of the foodservice operation's overall food safety system. Rejecting unacceptable products is necessary to decrease the risk of severe health consequences to customers.

Employees responsible for receiving food products must carefully inspect all incoming food supplies to make sure they are in acceptable condition. Products must be free from filth or spoilage and at the proper temperatures.

The first step to ensure proper receiving of food products is to set up a receiving program that follows these rules:

- Schedule deliveries during off-peak hours;
- Receive only one delivery at a time;
- Monitor the temperature of the delivery vehicle;
- Train staff to receive, inspect, and store food promptly;
- Check temperatures of the food items using a properly calibrated thermometer; and
- Label all items with the delivery date and store on a "first-in-first-out'" (FIFO) basis.

The trained receiver checks the delivery to ensure:

- The delivery truck is suitable for the purposes intended; is free of possible contaminants; and has the accurate temperature controls to maintain refrigerated food at 4° C (40° F) or lower and frozen foods at -18° C (0° F) or lower;
- There are no signs of temperature abuse during transport, such as large ice crystals, excess frost on packages and water stained boxes;
- There are no conditions that would allow potential contamination between the food products and the non-food products where both food and non-food products are transported together;
- All food products are labelled as described in the previous Control of Hazards Section 2.1;
- Packaging is intact. Improper packaging includes broken boxes, leaking packages, dented or swollen cans; and
- There are no visual signs of pest infestations or other food safety related factors such as expired "best before" dates.

4

Shipment Rejection

Any food that fails to meet product-receiving criteria (e.g. foods intended for frozen storage that show evidence of having been thawed) should be rejected for a credit note and returned to the supplier. The receiver should record the rejection incidence to trace any food safety hazard trends from particular suppliers. If a food safety hazard trend is discovered, then the foodservice operation should discontinue doing business with the supplier.

Receiving Guidelines for Different Foods:

Product	Acceptable Criteria
Dairy Products (Milk, butter, cheese)	• Fluid milk, fluid milk products, and soft cheeses must have been pasteurized. • Heat-treated hard aged cheeses are also acceptable. • Dry powdered milk and milk products may be reconstituted, but only under suitable conditions, where regulations permit. • Products not classed as milk products under The Dairy Products Act, such as margarine, butter substitutes, frozen dairy products, soft ice cream, yogurt and similar specialty foods, filled milk and milk substitutes, and cream substitutes are subject to the same requirements as dairy products, unless otherwise specified on the container.
Eggs and Egg Products	• Only inspected and graded eggs from approved poultry flocks are to be used. • Cracked eggs, grade C eggs, should not be purchased for use in a foodservice operation under any circumstances. Note: There may be an exception to this in jurisdictions where approved for use by the local regulatory agency. • Commercially prepared melange must not be used unless the manufacturer has pasteurized it and the container is marked accordingly.
Poultry and Poultry Products	• Must be purchased from approved sources. • Fresh poultry should be received packed on self-draining crushed ice or in chill packs.
Bakery and Bakery Products	• Must be prepared within the foodservice operation, or purchased from an inspected food-processing establishment or reputable bakery. Note: There may be an exception to this requirement in jurisdictions where products are approved for use by the regulatory agency.

Product	Acceptable Criteria
Canned and Other Hermetically Sealed Foods	• Must always be obtained from an approved commercial cannery. • No "in-house" canned or bottled foods may be used. • Can and seal should be received in good condition – no leaks, stains or dents in or on the can. Blown cans must never be used.
Shellfish and Other Marine Edible Foods	• Waters from which they are obtained and the premises in which they were handled and processed must meet federal regulations. • Seafood tags must be retained for a minimum of 90 days after use.
Sushi Fish and Sashimi	• Should be firm and springy to the touch with nothing more than a slight hint of fresh seawater smell. • Must not have a "fishy" smell. • Foodservice operator must ensure that their certified supplier blast freezes raw fish products at the correct time and temperature to eliminate parasitic microorganisms.
Produce (i.e. fruits and vegetables)	• Must be purchased and maintained free from insect infestation, dirt, mould, mushiness, discolouration, wilting, unpleasant odours and tastes. • Over-ripe products should be avoided.
Ice	• Must be manufactured from a water supply that meets Public Health bacteriological and chemical standards and must be handled, stored and transported in sanitary containers and protected from contaminants.

4

2.3. Disposition
Food products that have been inspected and found unclean, temperature abused, contaminated, damaged or in any way unsafe must be rejected or segregated and returned to the supplier or discarded and must not be available for consumption.

If unsafe foods are not removed immediately, keep them away from your safe consumable food and supplies to prevent contamination.

How to dispose of any rejected food items:

- Identify all unsafe food item with a label "Rejected – Do Not Use";
- Segregate the unsafe food away from safe food to minimize contamination; and
- Have the supplier pick up unsafe product or discard in garbage/waste.

3. Storage

3.1 Food Storage
Stock must be managed on a first-in-first-out (FIFO) basis. Spills and damaged products must be cleaned up or removed from food storage areas. Defective stock must be identified for suppliers for replacement and follow up.

Proper rotation of food stocks limits spoilage and potential infestation/contamination by pests. Proper rotation and inspection of food items reduces the risk of illness in customers. Quality and freshness also ensure a satisfied customer.

How to maintain the FIFO storage system?

- On each food package/box/container, write one of the following: 1) the expiration date; 2) when the item was received or 3) when it was stored after preparation.
- Shelve new supplies behind old, so the old products are used first.
- Regularly check expiration dates to ensure old product is being used first.
- Never use products past their expiration date.

MD

3.2. Refrigerated Storage
All potentially hazardous foods must be received and/or stored at a temperature of 4°C (40°F) or lower.

Temperature control is an effective way to prevent microbial growth and product deterioration. Keeping products at refrigerated temperatures helps to decrease the growth of microorganism in foods.

Foodservice operators should:

- Monitor food temperatures regularly. Using a calibrated thermometer (see Appendix C –Thermometer Calibration), take random temperatures of foods stored in the refrigerator and check the temperature of the refrigeration unit (read the unit's thermometer);
- Place two hanging thermometers inside the refrigerator; one in the back and one at the front by the refrigerator door;
- Never overload the refrigerator. Overloading may prevent airflow and make the unit work harder to keep product cold;
- Never line the shelving with foil or paper – these prevent airflow;
- Store raw meat, poultry, and fish separately from cooked and ready-to-eat foods to prevent cross-contamination;
- Establish the following top-to-bottom order in the refrigerator; Fish; whole cuts of beef: pork; ham, bacon and sausage; ground beef and ground pork; poultry; and
- Wrap foods properly. Leaving food uncovered can cause cross contamination. Food should be stored in clean, covered containers that are clearly marked.

MD

3.3. Frozen Storage

Frozen foods must be received and maintained in a solid frozen state at a temperature of -18°C (0°F) or less.

Frozen food must be stored at temperatures that will keep it frozen. To maintain frozen food, freezer temperatures must be at or below -18°C (0°F).

Foodservice operators should:

- Check the freezer unit regularly;
- Monitor freezer temperature daily;
- Rotate frozen food using the FIFO method;
- Check for damage to food from lengthy freezing;
- Keep the unit closed as much as possible; and
- Defrost freezers regularly. It is preferable to move food to another freezer while defrosting.

MD

3.4. Dry Food Storage

Foods not requiring refrigeration or frozen storage, must be stored in a clean, well ventilated, well lit, enclosed area, specifically designated for food storage.

Temperature control is an effective way to prevent microbial growth and product deterioration. To protect the food from pests, humidity and any other contamination, dry food should be stored in a designated storage room/area.

Foodservice operators should:

- Keep storerooms cool, dry, and well ventilated;
- Keep the temperature of the storeroom between 10°C to 21°C (50°F and 70°F). Avoid excessive high temperatures;
- Ensure the relative humidity is between 50 to 55 %;
- Store dry foods at least 15 cm (6 inches) off the floor away from direct sunlight and heat;
- Store foods in their original packages as much as possible.

Once the packages are opened, store the product in airtight containers that are clearly labelled;

- Remove exterior wrappings from supplies before storing them and dispose (see Section VI – Cleaning and Sanitation) of the wrapping immediately;
- Keep all foods stored in a closed container to prevent contamination or spread of food insects.
- Store foods according the first-in-first-out rule. Boxes and cans should all be labelled with the date of delivery.

MD

3.5. Chemical Storage
All chemicals must be stored under proper conditions in an area away from food and food contact surfaces.

4

Hazardous chemicals such as cleaners, sanitizers, pest control chemicals, floor polishers, degreasers, and other non-food chemicals can be poisonous and result in customer illness or death. Additional information on the storage of chemicals and other poisonous materials can be found in the Workplace Hazardous Materials Information System (WHMIS) guidelines.

Chemical storage:

- A dry, well lit, monitored area;
- Separate from food and food contact surfaces;
- Kept in original packaging with instructions; and
- Kept well covered after initial use to prevent contamination.

Storage Guidelines for Foods:

Foods must be kept at temperatures that minimize the growth of microbial pathogens. Food not requiring refrigeration or frozen storage must be stored in a clean, well ventilated, well lit, enclosed area specifically designated for food storage. The following table provides guidelines regarding proper storage of various foods.

Product	Acceptable Criteria (all temperatures quoted are internal product temperatures)
Raw foods (uncooked foods)	• Generally, store in refrigerated condition, 4°C (40°F), on a shelf below cooked and prepared foods.
Solid or semi-solid food items	• When stored in refrigerator, containers cannot be deeper than 10 cm (4 inches).
Canned and other hermetically sealed foods	• Rotate and observe stock. • Discard blown or swollen end cans. • Discard cans without labels. • Notify suppliers/manufacturers immediately of any abnormalities in canned goods. Note: some products in cans or glass containers require refrigeration, i.e. cured hams, corned beef, salted herring. Ensure to read the label for storage instructions.
Canned meats and canned meat products	• Generally, store at temperatures not above 21°C (70°F) – room temperature. • In the case of pasteurized products, keep at 4°C (40°F) or lower - refrigerator. • Once the can has been opened, the unused contents must be refrigerated.
Fresh meat, smoked or cured meat	• Store under sanitary refrigerated conditions at 4°C (40°F) or lower. • Once vacuum pack has been opened, refrigerate ground meat at 2°C (36°F) or lower for an optimal shelf life. Use within 72 hours.
Processed meat products with added preservatives	• Keep under refrigeration at 4°C (40°F) or lower.
Reconstituted dried meat products	• Keep under refrigeration at 4°C (40°F) or lower. • Used within 24 hours.
Cooked meat	• Keep cooked meat awaiting use at 4°C (40°F) or lower for no more than 72 hours.

	• Keep cooked ground meat at 2°C (36°F) or lower. This will assist in achieving the optimal shelf life.
	• Cooked meat awaiting use can be quick-frozen and held frozen solid until required.
Entrees containing meat and meat products	• Entrees made on premises and quick-frozen must be kept frozen solid until use. Frozen entrees must be kept in a frozen solid state and not be refrozen after defrosting.
Frozen meat and frozen meat products	• Keep in frozen solid state at -18°C (0°F) or lower until required for use.
	• Ideally, defrosted in a refrigerator at 4°C (40°F) or lower.
	• Store on bottom shelf when defrosting in the refrigerator.
	• Frozen uncooked meat and prepared meat may be refrozen if only partially thawed if ice crystals are still present, or the temperature is below 4°C (40°F), but not if such product has been held at room temperature for longer than two hours.
Vacuum packaged meats	Refrigerated:
	• Keep refrigerated at 4°C (40°F) or lower no longer than 18 days.
	• Keep ground meat at 2°C (36°F) or lower in an unopened vacuum pack for the optimal shelf life.
	• If a vacuum bag of an unfrozen meat product becomes broken, the product must be used within 72 hours.
	Frozen:
	• If freezing vacuum packaged meat, this should be done when the meat is packed, and not after a storage period.
	• Hold in frozen solid state at -18°C (0°F) or lower until required for use.
	• Never refreeze vacuum packaged meats or meat preparations under any circumstances.
	• Any vacuum-packed meat product that

4

	has been thawed at room temperature must be discarded as unfit for consumption.
	• Hold frozen products (originally frozen when the vacuum-packed meat was being processed at the plant of origin) for no longer than two months, with the exception of frozen beef roasts and beefsteaks, which can be held for six months. If the temperature is -18°C or colder, then the storage time can be double that recommended.
	• If a vacuum bag of a frozen meat product becomes broken, the product must be used within 72 hours.
Fresh or smoked poultry and poultry products	• Keep under refrigeration at 4°C (40°F) or lower for no longer 72 hours before use. • Because of the Salmonella hazard associated with poultry and poultry products, precautions must be observed during storage to prevent any spread of this bacterial infection from raw to cooked products, or to other foods.
Frozen poultry	• Keep solid frozen at -18°C (0°F) or lower. • Poultry may be defrosted as outlined in Section 5 of this document on thawing.
Fresh and frozen eggs and egg products	**Refrigerated:** • Keep stored at 4°C (40°F) or lower, and used within in one week of receipt. • Store egg products such as dried eggs and dried egg products, and commercially prepared, pasteurized melange at temperatures preferably 4°C (40°F) or lower and use within seven-day period of opening. • Do not transfer egg products from their original containers. Use them within seven days after opening. **Frozen:** • Keep in their original identified container until used. • Keep in frozen solid until use at -18°C

(0°F) or lower.
- Defrost at 4°C (40°F) or lower, and do not refreeze.
- Keep whites at 4°C (40°F) or lower and use within five days.
- Keep defrosted yolks and mixtures at 4°C (40°F) or lower and use within three days.

Fresh and frozen fluid milk and fluid milk products	Refrigerated: • Keep under refrigeration at 4°C (40°F) or lower. • Make sure containers are date coded and the operator understands the coding. Frozen: • Frozen milk products subjected to temperatures above 0°C (32°F) should be examined, and thawed products should be discarded.
Cheeses	• Keep wrapped or covered at all times. • Keep under refrigeration at 4°C (40°F) or lower.
Ice cream and frozen desserts	• Keep at −12°C (10°F) or lower until served. • Keep wrapped or covered in containers.
UHT (Ultra High Temperature Pasteurization) Foods	• These products when intact and unopened may be stored at room temperature.
Live fish	• If fish are maintained in live condition for later use, the water in which they are kept must be clean and aerated. • Saltwater fish must be maintained in salt water. • Tanks must be kept clean, and any dead fish discarded. Note: identify the optimal cleaning schedules for your specific fish tank. Also, identify the optimal length of time to keep each specific fish species in the tank (i.e. through supplier).

4

Fish and fish products	**Refrigerated:** • Keep fresh fish at 2°C (36°F) or lower. • Keep smoked fish at 4°C (40°F) or lower. • Vacuum pack smoked fish unless immediately frozen. • Keep sushi fish at 4°C (40°F) or lower. • Keep cooked fish awaiting use at 4°C (40°F) or lower for no more than 72 hours. **Frozen:** • Keep frozen fish in frozen solid until use, at -18°C (0°F). • Defrost at 4°C (40°F) or lower. • Use defrosted fish immediately and do not refreeze. • Cooked fish awaiting use may be quick-frozen and held solid until required.
Canned fish or fish products	• Keep at temperatures not above 21°C (70°F). • Use content of can upon opening, or else refrigerate and use within 24 hours.
Lobster	**Fresh:** • Maintain in live condition until used. • Keep at 4°C (40°F) or lower. **Frozen:** • Frozen cooked lobsters must be kept frozen solid, at -18°C (0°F) for the length of time specified by the supplier.
Mollusc and shellfish	• Keep alive until used if sold in the shell. • Keep at 4°C (40°F) or lower.
Shucked shellfish	• Keep in the original container under refrigeration or in frozen condition until used.
Fats and oils	• Keep in original containers, or in suitable approved bulk storage. • Keep at temperatures recommended for the particular product and its use. • Fats used for frying - keep clean and free from food particles.

	• Rendered fats prepared on the premises – chill rapidly and hold under refrigeration at 4°C (40°F) or lower in clean covered containers. • Discard rancid fats. • Store non-edible oils used for heating, lubricating, etc. in well-marked containers in well-designated areas away from food preparation. Note: since the chemical deterioration of fats and oils can create a fire hazard, used fats and oils should be discarded frequently, based on tests or consultation with the manufacturer.
Refrigerated bakery products Food mixtures prepared at a foodservice operation (e.g. combinations of prepared foods with dressings, mayonnaise, milk base sauces, gravies),	• Refrigerate Fillings and puddings at 4°C (40°F) or lower in shallow pans immediately after cooking or preparation, and hold refrigerated until combined into pastries or served. • Completed custards or cream-filled bakery products and those with edible oil simulated fillers continuously refrigerate at 4°C (40°F) or lower, unless served immediately following filling. Do not store longer than 48 hours. • If they contain poultry, eggs, meat, fish or other potentially hazardous foods, hold at 4°C (40°F) or lower for no more than 36 hours. • If prepared to be served cold, chill rapidly in one hour or less to an internal temperature of 4°C (40°F) or lower and hold at this temperature until use. Use within 36 hours. Do not refreeze.
Fruits and vegetables	• Separate fruit and vegetable handling and storage areas from other food handling areas. • Due to the higher possibility of insects, include in your storage cleaning program, weekly emptying and cleaning of the area, monitoring of insects and vermin, disposal of bags and other containers when empty. • Do not reuse empty bags and containers.

4

	• Do not store fruits and vegetables in plastic bags unless they are adequately ventilated.
	• Potatoes - It is recommended that long term storage be at 4°C (40°F) or lower and not exposed to light.
	• Canned fruit, vegetables or juices - keep at temperatures preferably 21°C (70°F) or lower. Once opened keep refrigerated at 4°C (40°F) or lower, and use within 72 hours.
	• Cooked fruit and vegetables or products - if not used at once keep at a temperature of 4°C (40°F) or lower for up to 48 hours. May be quick-frozen and held at −18°C (0°F) or lower until needed.
	• Frozen fruits, vegetables, juices and products - keep frozen at -18°C (0°F) or lower until used. If defrosting do it under refrigeration at 4°C (40°F) or lower. Do not refreeze defrosted products. Hold defrosted products under refrigeration and use within 48 hours.
Refrigerated "ready-to-eat"	• Mark with the date of preparation or the "consume by" date. All "ready-to-eat" food should be prepared and held for no longer than 24 hours.

4. Food Preparation

MD 4.1. Potentially hazardous foods must not be exposed to temperatures between 4°C (40°F) and 60°C (140°F) for longer than four hours maximum total accumulated time. During preparation, food must not be contaminated by other sources in the foodservice operation.

Food preparation is the step in which operators have the least amount of temperature control. Also, exposure to potential contamination from many sources such as food handlers, equipment, other food (raw or allergens) and the foodservice operation is possible. As foods are thawed, cooked, held, served, cooled and reheated, they may pass through the temperature danger zone of 4°C (40°F) and 60°C (140°F). Each time food is handled, it runs the risk of cross-contamination from other foods and from contaminated food contact surfaces.

In the foodservice operation, ensure that food preparation:

- Is completed in a quick, efficient manner to decrease time in the temperature danger zone of 4°C to 60°C (40°F to 140°F) and does not allow for processing delays (time of food in the temperature danger zone is cumulative);
- Is completed to avoid cross-contamination from other food products such as foods containing allergens or potentially hazardous raw foods; and
- Advance preparation time is as short as possible and all products made in advance are labelled to ensure the FIFO procedure is followed.

A Case in Point

A food-poisoning outbreak occurred at the local university cafeteria. A total of 13 students became ill and had the common symptoms of diarrhea and abdominal cramps. After an investigation it was concluded that they had all become sick from the shepherd's pie – the chef's special two days prior.

The Problem:
The hamburger meat used for the shepherd's pie was placed uncovered on the bottom shelf of the refrigerator to thaw. A tray of raw chicken was stored on the shelf just above the hamburger meat. The potatoes were cooked, then mashed – the chef noticed a long black hair in the potatoes. He took the hair out of the mashed potatoes and continued preparing the shepherd's pie. The shepherd's pie was cooked in a container with mild traces of dishwashing soap. After cooking, the shepherd's pie was left on the counter overnight at room temperature to cool. The next day the product was reheated to 140°F (60°C) and then served.

Solution:
The hamburger meat should not have been below the raw chicken and it should have been covered. The mashed potatoes should not have been used after finding the black hair. The cooking container should have been properly cleaned. The pie should have been stored in a refrigerated unit overnight and then reheated to 165°F (74°C) for serving.

Preparation Guidelines for Different Foods

Product	Acceptable Criteria
Salads and sandwiches	• Prepared foods such as salads or sandwiches should be made from chilled products, and with a minimum of manual contact.
Using sprouts	• As with many other foods, proper cooking kills bacteria. The risk of foodborne illness is significantly reduced when sprouts are cooked in soups, stir-frys and other dishes. • Raw sprouts have been linked to outbreaks of foodborne illness caused by Salmonella and Escherichia coli 0157:H7. If you plan to serve raw sprouts, it is important to use an approved supplier with good sanitary and manufacturing practices.
Bakery products	• Custards or cream-filled bakery products and those with edible oil simulated fillers that are potentially hazardous must be made with a minimum of manual contact. In addition, they should be made with utensils and equipment that have been thoroughly cleaned and sanitized. • Reconstituted dried egg products must be used immediately and should only be used in baking.
Food mixtures	• These mixtures may include combinations of prepared foods, with dressings, mayonnaise, milk base sauces, gravies or other approved foodstuffs. • Components of mixtures should be kept separate; mixing should be done as close as possible to planned time of use, particularly since one or more components may be highly perishable,

4

	and potentially hazardous.
	• Mixtures that require reheating must be reheated to 74°C (165°F) or higher and used within 24 hours.
	• All utensils used to prepare, handle or store mixtures of foods must be cleaned and sanitized before use and between each preparation.
Fresh fruits and vegetables	• Must be washed and spray rinsed thoroughly before use.
Egg and egg products	• It is a good practice to avoid serving raw eggs in preparations to be eaten by customers in a foodservice operation.
Meats and meat products	• Fresh meat that has been chopped or minced should be used within 24 hours, and all meat should be under regular inspection to ensure it remains safe for human consumption.
Sushi fish and sashimi	• Fish that is intended to be consumed raw, including raw-marinated and partially cooked fish must be purchased from a supplier in a frozen state that ensures parasitic destruction; or if being prepared on-site, frozen to a temperature of -20°C (-4° F) or below for 7 days; or to a temperature of -35°C (-31°F) or below for 15 hours in a blast freezer.
	• Must always be thawed in a refrigerator at 4°C (40°F) and prepared as quickly as possible.
	• Never make sushi with fresh water fish, such as trout, largemouth bass, catfish etc. Fresh water fish have been known to have parasites. Salmon, cod, herring and many more saltwater fish may also have parasites.
	• Should be firm and springy to the touch with nothing more than a slight hint of fresh seawater smell.
	• Must not have a "fishy" smell.

5. Thawing

MD

5.1. Potentially hazardous foods must be thawed quickly or in a manner that will prevent the rapid growth of pathogenic bacteria.

Food must be thawed in one of the following manners:

- Under refrigeration at 4°C (40°F) or less;
- Completely submerged in cold running potable water.
- Thawing as a part of the cooking process; and
- Using a microwave (be sure to follow manufacturer's instructions).

Improper thawing provides an opportunity for surviving bacteria in the food product to grow to harmful numbers and/or produce toxins. Thaw the food product under one of the four safe methods to prevent the growth of microorganisms and decrease the health risk to the customers.

How to safely thaw foods:

Refrigeration thawing
Ideally, frozen foods are best thawed under refrigeration temperatures below 4°C (40°F).

When thawing under refrigeration
- Store/thaw raw meat, poultry and fish separately from cooked and ready-to-eat foods to prevent cross-contamination.
- When thawing raw meat, poultry, and fish, they should be stored in the following top-to-bottom order in the refrigerator: fish; whole cuts of beef; pork; ham, bacon, and sausage; ground beef and ground pork; poultry.

Thawing with cold running water
- The accumulated time in the temperature danger zone (i.e. thawing, preparation, cooking) must not exceed 4 hours.
- Food may also be thawed while completely submerged in cold running potable water with velocity sufficient to shake any loose particles into the overflow.
- Large meat products should be left in their plastic wrapping.

- The sink must be large enough to allow the food item to be covered and the sink should have a standpipe for its drain.

Thawing as part of the cooking process

- Thawing as part of the conventional cooking process is not recommended for the following: 1) large quantities of food, 2) for meat, fish, poultry or 3) casseroles. This is because of the danger that internal temperatures may not reach levels to kill bacteria.
- Thawing as part of the cooking process is only allowed when the thawing process has been taken into consideration when determining the cooking time.

Microwave thawing

- Always follow the microwave manufacturer's instructions when using this method. Each make and style of microwave requires different defrosting times and intensities. Foods thawed in the microwave should be cooked immediately.

Thawing Guidelines for Different Foods

Product	Acceptable Criteria
Poultry	• Can be safely refrozen if ice crystals are still present. • Takes poultry 10 hours /kg (4.5 hours/lb.) to thaw under the refrigeration method. • Takes poultry about two hours per kg. (less than one hour/lb.) to thaw under running water. • Products must be thawed on the bottom shelf of the refrigerator, under cooked and "ready-to-eat" products • Keep in mind that some frozen items such as large turkeys must be taken from the freezer up to four days before preparation.

Thawing eggs or egg products	• Must be defrosted at 4°C (40°F) or lower. • Defrosted eggs should never be refrozen. • Defrosted egg whites must be used within five days. • Defrosted yolks and mixtures must be used within three days.
Frozen fruits, vegetables and fruit/vegetable products	• Defrosting should be done under refrigeration at 4°C (40°F) or lower. • Defrosted products must not be refrozen. • Defrosted fruit, vegetable and juice products must be held under refrigeration.
Frozen mixtures	• Fresh-made mixtures (combinations of prepared foods with dressings, mayonnaise, milk base sauces, gravies or other approved foodstuffs) must be defrosted at 4°C (40°F) or lower and held at this temperature until use. • Mixtures must be used within 36 hours. • Mixtures must not be refrozen.
Meats and meat products	• Frozen meat products should be defrosted in a refrigerator at 4°C (40°F) or lower. • Frozen uncooked meat and prepared meat may be refrozen if only partially thawed, which means ice crystals are still present, or the temperature is below 4°C (40°F), but not if such product has been held at room temperature for longer than two hours. • Meat products must be thawed on a shelf of the refrigerator, under cooked and "ready-to-eat" products.

4

Vacuum packed food products	• Any vacuum-packed food product that has been thawed at room temperature must be discarded as unfit for consumption. • Vacuum packaged meats or meat preparations must never be refrozen.
Fish	• Frozen ready-to-eat seafood should be thawed at 3°C (38°F). • Frozen fish must be defrosted at 4°C (40°F) or lower. • Defrosted fish must be used immediately and not refrozen.

6. Cooking

6.1. Raw foods of animal origin and food mixtures containing raw foods of animal origin must be cooked to heat all parts of the food to the minimum temperatures and for the minimum times outlined.

Heat penetrates different foods at different rates. This means the "killing ability" of heat is affected by the characteristics of the food. For example, the effective killing ability of heat is reduced in foods of high fat. Also, different microorganisms have different susceptibilities to heat. In order to kill all pathogens in food, the cooking process needs to bring all parts of the food up to the required temperatures for the correct length of time. In general, high humidity within the cooking pan and foods with moisture content help with microbial pathogen destruction.

The best ways to achieve the suggested cooking temperature, and thus destroy pathogenic bacteria, is to:
• Cook food in small batches;
• Agitate or stir when cooking large quantities of liquids or semi-liquids;
• Cook in one continuous process (i.e. whole turkeys and large cuts of beef); or
• Cook dressings (i.e. stuffing) separately because they act as an insulator and keep part of the food in the temperature danger zone.

Cooking Guidelines for Different Foods

Pathogen reduction involves a time-temperature relationship. Other times and temperatures may be acceptable, if considered equivalent and approved by the local regulatory authority.

Product	Acceptable Criteria
Poultry	• Health Canada recommends that poultry be cooked to a minimum internal temperature of 85°C (185°F) for 15 seconds; however, some concerns exist about product quality when poultry is exposed to these temperatures. Consequently, local regulatory authorities may stipulate different temperature requirements. Contact your local health regulator to determine the internal temperatures specified by your local regulatory authority. • A probe-type thermometer should be placed deeply under the drumstick. • All stuffing or other dressings should be cooked separately from the poultry.
Ground/flaked meats. Includes chopped, ground, flaked or minced beef, pork, or fish.	• A minimum temperature of 70°C (158°F) is required. • Thoroughly cook all ground meat products until all the pink is gone and the juices are clear.
Cooking mixtures includes combinations of prepared foods with dressings, mayonnaise, milk base sauces, gravies.	• If mixtures contain poultry, eggs, meat, fish or other potentially hazardous foods, these mixtures must be cooked to a minimum internal temperature of at least 74°C (165°F).
Whole cuts of meat includes: whole cuts of pork, lamb, veal and beef.	• Whole cuts of meat require a minimum internal temperature of 70°C (158°F).

Eggs	• Eggs require a minimum internal temperature of 63°C (145°F). • Customers requesting a runny yolk egg must be informed that pathogens are not destroyed until the yolk has been completely cooked.
Fish	• Fish requires a minimum internal temperature of 70°C (158°F). • Customers wishing raw marinated fish and raw mollusc and shellfish should be aware that it should be made cooked to assure food safety.

MD

6.2 Microwave cooking and reheating
Microwaves can be used for cooking and reheating.

Microwave cooking requires different consideration than conventional cooking. The rapid increase in food temperatures resulting from microwave heating does not provide the same cumulative time and temperature relationship necessary for the destruction of microorganisms compared to conventional cooking methods. Also, cold spots may exist in food cooking in a microwave oven. In order to achieve comparable heat destruction time, the food must attain a higher temperature.

To verify the internal temperature of the product, it is critical to measure the temperature of the food at multiple sites (middle, each side, front and back) after the food is removed from the microwave oven.

Potentially hazardous food cooked or reheated in a microwave must be:

* Rotated or stirred throughout or midway through the cooking process; and
* Allowed to stand covered for a minimum of two minutes after cooking.

To ensure the food reaches the recommended time and temperature relationship when microwave cooking, it is important to:

- Stir periodically to promote uniform heating of liquids and avoid cold spots;
- Heat to elevated temperatures (as per manufacturers' instructions) to compensate for shorter cooking times;
- Keep foods covered to allow thermal equalization and exposure; and
- Measure internal temperature at multiple sites when the food is removed from the oven to ensure no potential cold spots.

Note that microwave ovens lose their power over time, and therefore temperature levels and even cooking should be checked periodically.

7. Hot-Holding

MD

7.1. Potentially hazardous foods that have been prepared, cooked, and are to be served hot, must be held at a temperature of at least 60°C (140°F) until served.

Improper hot holding, below 60°C (140°F), is a common cause contributing to foodborne illness.
Pathogenic microorganisms can grow well in the temperature danger zone 4°C (40°F) to 60°C (140°F)

Hot holding equipment includes: steam tables, double boilers, bain maries, heated cabinets and chafing dishes.

Foods are to be served above 60°C (140°F). To maintain this temperature, the hot holding unit temperature needs to be even higher than 60°C (140°F). Measure the food temperature with a calibrated thermometer every two hours.

Good practices to follow during hot-holding include:
- Using hot holding equipment only to hold hot foods. It is not designed to cook food;
- Never mix new food with old food when restocking the hot holding equipment;

- Never mix raw food with cooked food;
- For food on display (i.e. buffet service) an additional protection against potential contamination such as coughing or sneezing can be provided by the use of sneeze guards on the food display units; and
- Minimize keeping food in hot holding equipment for more than 2 hours.

A Case in Point

A hospital had an outbreak of Salmonella poisoning that affected 10 people. They had all eaten the turkey dinner two evenings prior to the onset of the illness. The turkey dinner included turkey, mashed potatoes and cooked vegetables. During the investigation, the following facts were discovered: the turkeys were prepared in the same area as the fresh vegetables, a mop and bucket containing dirty water with cleaning chemicals were found in the preparation area, the cooking equipment had not been cleaned and sanitized before cooking the turkeys, the thermometer on the cooking equipment did not work, and the turkeys were held in a separate warmer for about seven hours. The temperature logbook did not contain any information for the past three days up to and including the time that the product had been cooked.

The Problem:
The employee/employees neglected to follow essential food safety steps.

Solution:
The turkeys should have been prepared in a separate area from raw vegetables and cleaning agents. The turkeys could have been contaminated with the Salmonella at this point. Furthermore, this action created an opportunity to contaminate the vegetables in the meal with Salmonella from raw turkey. The cooking equipment should have been fully cleaned, sanitized and functional prior to use. It is essential to take and note cooking temperatures during the cooking process to ensure the service of a safe product. The turkey shouldn't have been held in a warmer for seven hours. The warmer should have been checked with a calibrated thermometer and logged at least every two hours.

8. Cold-Holding

MD
8.1. All potentially hazardous foods must be stored at a temperature of 4°C (40°F) or less.

Foods requiring "cold-holding" include cold food that has been previously cooked (i.e. sliced turkey or roast beef) and foods consumed without cooking (i.e. salads or sandwiches). By keeping these foods at 4°C (40°F) or less, they are out of the temperature danger zone.

Good practices to follow during cold-holding include:

- The temperature of foods kept in cold-holding (i.e. salad bar) need to be measured with a calibrated thermometer every two hours.
- When using ice to hold "ready-to-eat" cold foods, never put the product directly on the ice. Put the foods in pans or on plates.
- For food on display (i.e. buffet service), an additional protection against potential contamination (such as coughing or sneezing) can be provided by the use of sneeze guards on the food display units.
- Not holding cold food on display (i.e. salad bar) for more than two hours.

9. Room Temperature Holding

MD
9.1. Potentially hazardous foods intended for immediate consumption, may be held for service (not kept on ice or other equivalent methods):
  - But for no more than two hours, after which they must be discarded; and
  - Foods must be marked with the time at which they were removed from temperature control.

The majority of microorganisms can double in number every 20 minutes while being held in the temperature danger zone. Some microorganisms can double every seven minutes. However, foods with low initial bacterial levels, that have undergone superior handling, cooking and/or chilling, may be held without temperature control for a short period of time. It is somewhat unlikely that significant growth of pathogens or toxin production is possible in a very limited time. Furthermore, products removed from proper refrigeration or cooking can hold these temperatures for a limited period of time.

Room temperature holding is a very high-risk activity that must be monitored closely. Tracking and keeping records of the products and the time at which they were removed from temperature control (such as cooking or refrigeration) must be recorded. The products exposure to the temperature danger zone (room temperature) must be limited to a cumulative time exposure of no more than two hours. This means that a product cannot be held for 1.5 hours, returned to refrigeration and then put on display for another two hours. In this example, the cumulative time exposure to the temperature danger zone would have been 3.5 hours. The product should have been discarded after two hours.

Hold foods intended for immediate consumption in a manner that prevents them from being contaminated (i.e. cover the food product to prevent exposure to microbiological, chemical or physical hazards).

Marking the food with the time it was removed from temperature control (i.e. refrigeration or cooking) is essential when monitoring the time it has been at room temperature.

10. Cooling

MD

10.1 Cooling after Cooking
Cooked potentially hazardous foods, intended for refrigerated storage prior to serving, must be cooled from 60°C (140°F) to 20°C (68°F) or less within two hours and then from 20°C (68°F) to 4°C (40°F) or less within four hours. It is important to note the cumulative time that a food product is left in the temperature danger zone.

Excessive time for cooling potentially hazardous foods has been consistently identified as one of the leading causes of foodborne illnesses. During extended cooling, potentially hazardous foods are subject to the growth of a variety of pathogenic microorganisms, which may grow to a sufficient number to cause illness.

In a foodservice operation, foods that are not served right away need to be cooled as quickly as possible and within the specified parameters.

To accelerate cooling, follow these procedures:

- Cut large items into smaller pieces;
- Divide larger liquid food batches into several smaller amounts in pre-chilled stainless steel pans;
- Place food items in blast chiller; and
- Stir food items with ice paddles
- Pre-cool large quantities of food using an ice-water bath;
- Accelerate cooling of large quantities of liquid and semi-liquids by stirring (using a cleaned and sanitized utensil);
- Cool foods, especially gravies, soups and casseroles, in shallow pans with the greatest surface area possible (no higher than four inches);
- Pre-slice turkey, chicken and roasts and place in shallow pans to allow quicker cooling; and
- Always cover food being cooled. Never use cloths to cover foods.

MD

10.2 Cooling from room temperature potentially hazardous foods prepared at room temperature, intended for refrigerated storage prior to serving, must be cooled from 20°C (68°F) to 4°C (40°F) or less within four hours.

Excessive time for cooling potentially hazardous foods has been consistently identified as one of the leading causes of foodborne illnesses. During extended cooling, potentially hazardous foods are subject to the growth of a variety of pathogenic microorganisms, which may grow to a sufficient number to cause illness.

Foods prepared at room temperature with ingredients which are canned or made from reconstituted foods must be cooled to 4°C (40°F) or less within four hours. An example of such food would be tuna or salmon sandwich filling made with canned fish.

11. Reheating

MD

11.1. Reheating for Hot Holding
- Reheat products to an internal temperature of at least 74°C (165°F) or higher.
- Ensure food passes through the temperature danger zone 4°C (40°F) to 60°C (140°F) within two hours.

The potential for growth of pathogenic bacteria is greater in reheated foods than in raw foods. Most bacteria are killed during the original cooking process. However, any subsequent contamination (i.e. contamination from a food handler sneezing on the product) that may have occurred in the product after the original cooking process may now be allowed to grow if temperature abuse occurs.

A foodservice operator should:

- Reheat all previously cooked food to an internal temperature of at least 74°C (165°F) or higher;
- Use cooking ranges, ovens, steamers, and microwaves to reheat food. Never use hot-holding equipment because it is not designed to reach and maintain the necessary temperatures; and
- Transfer reheated food to holding equipment only when the food is at 74°C (165°F) or higher.

In a foodservice operation there may be fully cooked outsourced items. If manufactured under safe conditions such as a certified Hazard Analysis Critical Control Point (HACCP) system, these can be safely re-heated to a temperature of 60°C (140°F).

- Foods that have been cooked, and then cooled to 4°C (40°F) once, can be served, if for immediate service, at any temperature, provided the time the food spends between 4°C (40°F) and 60°C (140°F) does not exceed two hours.
- Always pre-heat hot holding equipment before inserting hot food.
- Foods that have been cooked, cooled to 4°C (40°F), reheated and then re-cooled to 4°C (40°F) must be reheated to 74°C (165°F) or higher before being served for immediate consumption.

- Foods reheated for immediate service must not be between 4°C (40°F) and 60°C (140°F) for more than two hours.
- Foods must be reheated to 74°C (165°F) or higher.
- Reheated food items for immediate service must maintain a minimum internal temperature of 60°C (140°F).

12. Service

MD

12.1. Food handlers must avoid touching tableware, such as cups, glasses and cutlery, or setting the service area in a manner which could potentially contaminate the surfaces that come in contact with the consumer.

Every effort must be made to prevent unnecessary handling of soiled items to lessen the hazards of contaminating non-soiled items or surfaces. Cross contamination can cause serious foodborne illnesses in customers. This is important to note in a buffet service style establishment as both customers and employees need to handle serving utensils/dishware.

To provide a safe food environment during service, ensure:

- Clean paper or linen place settings are used for every new customer;
- Bare table surfaces are wiped with a sanitized wiping cloth between each use;
- Serving trays or cafeteria trays are sanitized in the same manner as dishes to avoid contaminating items carried on the tray; and
- Condiment containers and menus are kept clean.

Ensure service personnel understand the risk of cross contamination. Discuss the following tips for avoiding potential cross-contamination:

- Deliver and/or remove soiled dishes, glassware and cutlery in a manner that avoids the clean fingers of the server coming in contact with any soiled portion of the item.
- When clearing tables or counters place soiled tableware in suitable receptacles. These receptacles are to be of such

material and construction that they can be on stands, shelves or trucks, never stored directly on the floor.

- Keep soiled items separate from clean items at all times.
- Regard all tableware that has been part of any table setting, whether used or not, as soiled and handle as such.
- Do not place plates of food on top of glasses or cups.
- Use clean cutlery, gloves, and dishes for table service from a stored location set up to prevent contamination.
- Discard any item of food that is served but not consumed (except unopened, sealed, single service items).

Service/Dispensing Ice:

- When serving or dispensing ice never let your hands come in contact with the ice. Use appropriate utensils such as plastic or metal scoops.
- Never re-use ice.

Service of Milk and Milk Products:

- Serve fluid milk or milk products used for drinking purposes in the individual sealed containers in which they were packed at the dairy, or from dispensing equipment, such as covered pitchers, which have been approved for this purpose by health authorities.
- Serve cream, whipped cream, half and half, and milk that is used for coffee, tea or other beverages in containers provided by the dairy or from a dispenser approved by the health authority for such service. Make sure such containers or dispensers are refrigerated after use at 4°C (40°F) or lower.
- Discard milk, fluid milk products, cream and cream products removed for any purpose from their original containers or dispenser and not consumed.
- Discard any unused served portions of ice cream and frozen desserts. Do not expose bulk quantities to contaminated utensils or adverse temperature while serving.

13. Food Distribution

HR

13.1. Food transportation, storage and distribution units should be designed, constructed, maintained and used in a manner that protects food products from being contaminated.

Food can be seriously contaminated, or existing microbial contamination can be permitted to increase to dangerous levels, by unsanitary or careless distribution. Foods should be packaged in a way to prevent contamination and temperature control should be maintained during distribution.

Foods should not be accepted at a foodservice operation unless distributed in the following manner:

4

- Packaged in such a way that contamination is prevented during distribution.
- Transported under required conditions i.e. refrigerated or frozen. (See Section IV- Control of Hazards)

If food and non-food products are distributed together, ensure that food products are not exposed to the potential contamination from non-food products.

Section V
Equipment and Utensils

V. Equipment and Utensils

1. Equipment Location and Installation

MD

1.1 Equipment used in a food premises must be located so that it:

- Is not exposed to any sources of contamination unrelated to the normal operation of the food premises;
- May be maintained, cleaned, and sanitized;
- May be conveniently inspected;
- May be properly vented when required; and
- Is properly sealed to adjoining surrounding, if equipment is fixed.

It is important that equipment be conveniently located to allow for easy cleaning and thus eliminate harbourage of microorganisms and other contaminants.

Store moveable equipment that is used in processing, handling, and storage of foods in areas where the equipment does not become contaminated. Areas where equipment could become contaminated include: staff locker rooms, toilet rooms, garbage storage rooms, mechanical rooms, under sewer or water lines not shielded to intercept leakage/condensate, under open stairwells.

Fixed equipment, or equipment not intended to be easily moved, needs to be placed in a manner that prevents harbourage of microorganisms and other contaminations:

- Attach fixed equipment to surrounding walls, floors, or other equipment; or
- Space it in a manner to allow for cleaning under and around equipment and prevent the accumulation of dirt.

Some equipment requiring a more permanent installation may need to be in accordance with local building and fire ordinances (see local regulatory agency for further information).

2. Equipment and Utensil Design

MD

2.1 Equipment and utensils must be designed and constructed to be durable and to retain their characteristic qualities under foodservice operational use and conditions and perform as intended.

It is important that equipment design allow for clean and sanitary conditions. Also, it is important that equipment performs as intended. If the equipment is not designed with food safety in mind, the equipment can cause biological hazards such as E.coli. If for example, the cooking equipment does not allow the required temperature and time to be reached and microorganisms are not destroyed. Equipment could also cause physical hazards from equipment with removable components.

Check the design of the equipment used in the foodservice operation or equipment to be purchased so it:

- Has the capacity to achieve and/or maintain the required food temperatures to cook, heat treat, cool, store or freeze potentially hazardous foods, as described by law;
- Is equipped with monitoring and controlling temperatures devices, i.e. for heating and cooling equipment;
- Is suitable for the intended purpose;
- Any removable components, such as drip pans, lids, knife blades, shields or panels, meet the requirements of health authorities; and
- All internal surfaces are self-draining, and/or easily reached by normal cleaning and sanitizing processes.

If the foodservice operation uses any applicable household appliance not specifically designed for use in a commercial setting, ensure the appliance complies with international sanitation standards, such as those administered by third parties (i.e. NSF International (NSFI) and Underwriters' Laboratories of Canada (ULC) and CSA (Canadian Standards Association).

5

Ensure that the surfaces of food equipment that do not come in direct contact with the food are designed and constructed to further minimize the likelihood of food contamination and are:
- Free from unnecessary ledges, projections, and crevices; and
- Designed to allow easy cleaning and maintenance.

Equipment Design Guidelines:

Equipment	Acceptable Criteria
Clean-in-place equipment	• Cleaning and sanitizing solutions should circulate through a fixed system and contact all interior food contact surfaces. • The system or equipment should be self-draining or capable of being completely drained of cleaning and sanitizing solutions. • There should be inspection access points to ensure all interior food contact surfaces throughout the fixed system or equipment are being effectively cleaned.
Filters and grease extraction equipment	• Exhaust ventilation hood systems (i.e. hoods, fans, guards, ducting) should be designed to prevent grease or condensation from draining or dripping onto food and food contact surfaces. • Must be designed to be readily removable for cleaning and replacement (National Building Code and the National Fire Prevention Act 96). • Ventilation hood systems must be sufficient in number and capacity to prevent grease or condensation from collecting on walls and ceilings.

Heating and cooling equipment	<ul><li>Must be designed and operated to achieve and maintain the required food temperatures (See Section III-Construction, Design, and Facilities).</li><li>If equipment impacts food safety, it must be equipped with devices to monitor and control temperatures.</li><li>Temperature measuring devices on the equipment must be easily readable and accurate to 1.0°C (2.0°F) in the operating range (See Appendix C – Thermometer Calibration).</li></ul>

MD

2.2. Food contact surfaces of equipment and utensils must not introduce substances into food that are harmful or change food characteristics.

5

The food contact surfaces should not be the source introducing harmful substances into the food. Copper (due to copper migration), cast iron (due to heavy metals migration into the food), lead glazed utensils and galvanized metals are all areas of concern. Food preparation or serving surface, utensils or containers can introduce foreign matter into food items. If a restaurant cook is preparing a pizza on a wooden surface that is old and flaking, customers may receive wooden particles that could cause serious physical harm.

Ensure that the food contact surfaces:

- Are corrosion resistant, smooth, non-absorbent and easily cleanable to eliminate harbourage for microorganisms and other contaminants;
- Non-toxic, free from pitting, cracks and crevices;
- Do not introduce substances into food, such as colour, odours and tastes or substances (metals) which are harmful; and
- Are durable for the safe preparation and cooking of the food.

Wooden Food Contact Surfaces

Wooden food contact surfaces are not normally acceptable or recommended for cutting, especially for meat and poultry. Moist foods may cause the wood surface to deteriorate and the surface to become difficult to clean, leading to contamination on the cutting board.

Then how can wood be used in a food premise?

Hard maple or an equivalently hard, close-grained wood may be used for: cutting boards; cutting blocks; baker's tables; and utensils such as rolling pins, doughnut dowels, salad bowls, chopsticks, and wooden paddles that are used in confectionery operations for pressure scraping kettles when manually preparing confections at temperature of 110°C (230°F) or above.

Surfaces such as cutting blocks and boards that are subject to scratching and scoring should be resurfaced if they can no longer be effectively cleaned and sanitized, or discarded if they are not capable of being resurfaced.

3. Maintenance

3.1. Equipment must be maintained in good repair, so that it functions in accordance with its intended use.

Foodservice operations need to periodically check equipment to make sure it is not causing any unknown contamination. Outside foodservice operation services might be required for major equipment maintenance.

When maintaining and replacing, check that food contact surfaces are:

- Smooth, free from cracks, crevices, pitting or unnecessary indentations;
- Made of a material resistant to insects or rodents;
- Resistant to the acids and alkalis normally attendant on food preparation;
- Resistant to damage through normal usage;
- Made of non-toxic, non-absorbent materials; and
- Made with non-flaking or peeling finish with joints in

surfaces that are flush, and if soldered, welded or bonded, non-toxic materials.

Manufacturer's manuals outlining maintenance procedures should be readily available for each piece of equipment and instructions should be strictly adhered to.

See Section VI - Cleaning and Sanitation Section for Cleaning Equipment/Food Contact Surfaces details.

See Section IV - Control of Hazard Section for Utensil Storage details.

4. Calibration

MD

4.1. All heating and cooling equipment must be calibrated on a regular basis to ensure correct functioning.

Equipment used to heat or store potentially hazardous foods at safe temperatures must have the capacity to raise or lower the temperature of the food to safe levels as quickly as possible. If equipment cannot reach or maintain the desirable safe food product temperatures, then there is an increased risk of bacterial growth leading to the possibility of foodborne illness when the food is consumed.

- Equipment used to store potentially hazardous foods at safe temperatures needs to be calibrated according to manufacturer specification so as to ensure continual safe product temperatures.
- All temperature measuring devices (including portable thermometers) must be calibrated on a routine basis.
- Temperature measuring devices must be easily readable and accurate to 1.0°C (2°F).
- A good calibration program includes recording the calibration results, as well as any corrective action taken, for each piece of equipment.

Food temperature measuring devices should not have sensors or stems constructed of glass unless they are encased in a shatterproof sleeve.

See Appendix C - Temperature Checking and Thermometer Calibration

5

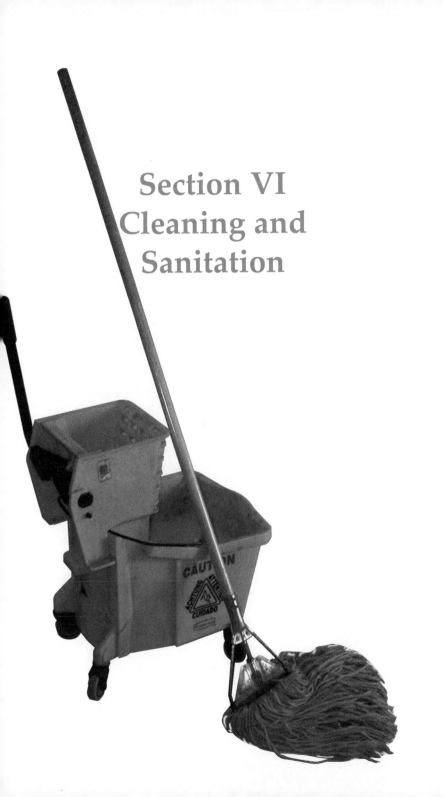

Section VI
Cleaning and
Sanitation

VI - Cleaning And Sanitation

1. Cleaning Program for Facilities and Equipment

MD

1.1. A foodservice operation must have an effective system in place to ensure adequate and appropriate cleaning of the facility and equipment.

Food is easily contaminated, therefore it is essential that all equipment and utensils, particularly those that come in contact with food, be regularly cleaned and sanitized. Effective cleaning and sanitizing requires that visible soil be removed and microorganisms, which are invisible, be destroyed. To prevent dangerous contamination of food from food contact surfaces, utensils and equipment, an efficient cleaning and sanitizing program must be carried out on a regular schedule, using effective materials. Furthermore, since unclean facilities can contaminate food contact surfaces, they also need to be cleaned and sanitized regularly.

An effective cleaning program has written procedures or instructions for staff on how to clean and sanitize the facility, equipment, utensils, and things like refrigeration units that impact food safety.

These procedures/instructions should specify:

- Areas or items of equipment and utensils to be cleaned (noting high risk areas);
- The designated foodhandler(s) responsible for cleaning and sanitizing;
- The chemicals and/or cleaning products (including concentrations) and process to be used;
- The procedures used, whether clean-in-place (CIP) or clean-out-of-place (COP) (including temperatures and time for cleaning);
- The equipment required to do the cleaning;
- The frequency of cleaning and sanitizing;
- Records to be completed after cleaning and sanitizing; and
- Inspection and monitoring of equipment and records to confirm or verify that the cleaning was effective.

You can develop a master cleaning schedule for all cleaning operations and equipment. *A Cleaning on the Dot Chart* is available from the CRFA.

The following points that are important to include in your cleaning program:

- Food contact surfaces (exclusive of cooking surfaces), utensils, equipment are to be cleaned after each use;
- Cutting and chopping boards require special care around cleaning and sanitizing because they are hard to clean and can be sources of cross contamination. Equipment and utensils used continuously at room temperature preparation or service (i.e. deli meat slicers) require cleaning and sanitizing at least every four hours;
- Removable safety guards or shields must be removed when the unit is cleaned;
- Infrequently used or stored equipment/utensils must be cleaned and sanitized before being used; and
- Polished materials (i.e. knives, forks) that come in contact with food need to be cleaned and sanitized prior to use.

2. Cleaning Reusable Food Equipment & Utensils

MD

2.1. Cleaning processes for all reusable food equipment and utensils must include cleaning (removal of food residues and dirt), rinsing and sanitization (by heat or chemical means). The process, whether done manually or mechanically, must include all of these steps.

The step of cleaning only serves to remove food debris through mechanical action or by dissolving food ingredients such as sugars in water or fats in alkali cleaners. The sanitization step kills the bacteria that were not removed during the cleaning step. If equipment is cleaned but not sanitized, bacteria will still grow. The rinsing step removes soap from washing, which could make the sanitizer solution ineffective. If the surface is treated with sanitizer but not cleaned, then the food debris will neutralize the effect of the sanitizer and render it useless.

Equipment Cleaning Criteria:

All food contact equipment and utensils used in the preparation, service, display, or storage of food must be cleaned and sanitized after each use. Food contact surfaces of cooking equipment need to be cleaned and sanitized as often as is necessary to prevent the accumulation of grease deposits and other residues. However, some types of equipment such as pizza pans or baking dishes, which do not pose a public health risk, may be cleaned less frequently.

Clean-in-Place (CIP) Equipment:

Some equipment, such as ice machines or soft-serve ice cream machines, is designed to be cleaned in place by flushing detergent, hot water and sanitizing solution through it. This process should be done daily unless otherwise indicated by the manufacturer. Cleaning and sanitizing solutions must:

- Remain within a fixed system of pipes for a predetermined amount of time.
- Not leak into the rest of the machine.
- Reach all food-contact surfaces.

There are two main methods used to clean and sanitize equipment and utensils.

1. Manual Dishwashing

Where manual dishwashing procedures are used for cleaning and sanitizing cooking utensils, dishware and serving/dining utensils, the manual dishwashing setup should include:

- At least a double sink of non-corrodible metal of sufficient size (length, width, depth), to allow complete immersion of the utensils to be sanitized.

Note: a three-compartment sink is preferred, however, a two-compartment sink is allowed under conditions where it has been established that washing and rinsing can be done effectively in the first sink and the second sink is used for sanitizing. (Consult your local health authority for further information);

- Shelving and sinks with drain boards made of non-corrodible metal, constructed to withstand the weight of utensils and dishware without buckling, and sloped for self-drainage;
- A large enough space for holding soiled utensils. This space must be separated from areas used for stacking and holding clean utensils;
- A clock with a second hand or a timer should be available for the employees to time how long items have been immersed in the sanitizing sink;
- A thermometer capable of measuring temperatures between 0°C and 100°C (32°F and 212°F); and
- Testing equipment to determine the strength of any chemical used as the sanitizing agent.

It is recommended that manual dishwashing instruction card be on permanent display above the dishwashing area to guide the washer.

Manual dishwashing procedures include the following steps:

1. Pre-rinse step:
Sort, scrape, and pre-rinse utensils free of food scraps.

2. Wash step:
Wash dishes, utensils, etc. in the first sink compartment with detergent solution capable of removing grease and food particles. Maintain at a temperature of not less than 45°C (113°F) or above.

3. Rinse Step:
Rinse dishes, utensils, etc. in the second compartment sink in clean, potable (safe-to-drink) water maintained at a temperature of not less than 45°C (113°F) or above.

4. Sanitizing Step:
Sanitize dishes, utensils, etc. in the third sink compartment by one of the following methods:

i)   Immerse for at least two minutes in hot water that sanitizes dishes using a basket or rack at a temperature of 77°C (171°F).

OR

ii) Immerse for at least two minutes in a chlorine solution of 100 – 200 mg/l (ppm) of available chlorine at a temperature of not less than 45°C (113°F).

OR

iii) Immerse for at least two minutes in a quaternary ammonium compound solution of 200 mg/l (ppm) at a temperature that is specified by the chemical manufacturer.

OR

iv) Immerse for at least two minutes in an iodine solution of 25 mg/ml (ppm) at a temperature of not less than 45°C (113°F).

OR

v)   Use other sanitizing procedures that have been scientifically proven to produce results equivalent to those achieved by use of the above methods, and which have been approved by the local health authority.

5) Allow utensils to air-dry.

2. Mechanical Dishwashing

Mechanical dishwashing procedures include the following methods:

Chemical Sanitizing Method:

Mechanical dishwashing machines use chemicals to sanitize tableware, utensils and equipment. Apply the sanitizing solution as follows:

i) Chlorine Solution used as a sanitizing agent should have the following:

Minimum Concentration mg/l (ppm)	Minimum Temperature pH 8 to 10	Minimum Temperature pH 8 or less
25	49° C (120°F)	49° C (120°F)
50	38° C (100°F)	24°C (75°F)
100	13°C (55°F)	13° C (55°F)

ii) Iodine solution used as a sanitizing agent should have:

Concentration mg/1 (ppm)	Minimum pH	Minimum Temperature
12.5 mg/l (ppm) to 25 mg/l (ppm)	5.0 or less, or as indicated manufacturer's specifications	24°C (75°F)

iii) Quaternary Ammonium compound solution used as a sanitizing agent should have:

Concentration mg/1 (ppm)	Water Hardness Concentration	Minimum Temperature
200 mg/l (ppm) or as indicated in the manufacturer's specifications	less than 500 mg/l (ppm)	24°C (75°F)

6

The operator should check the temperatures of the water and the sanitizer concentration frequently to ensure that effective results are occurring.

The operator should keep records of sanitizer concentrations and temperatures.

Sanitizer test kits/strips should be obtained from the sanitizer/detergent supplier and stored for convenient use near the dishwasher.

3. Hot Water Sanitizing Method:

When using a mechanical dishwashing machine with hot water sanitization of tableware, utensils and equipment, make sure the following specifications are met:

Temperature of the wash solution in spray type washers must not be less than:

- 74°C (165°F), for a stationary rack, single temperature machine
- 66°C (151°F), for a stationary rack, dual temperature machine
- 71°C (160°F), for a single tank, conveyor, dual temperature machine
- 66°C (151°F), for multi-tank, conveyor, multi-temperature machine
- Rinse water exposure must be to 74°C (165°F) for 10 seconds for single tank, stationary rack, single temperature machines and 82°C (179°F) for 10 seconds for all other machines.

3. Single-service Utensils and Containers

MD

3.1 Single-service utensils and containers must not be used more than once. This is to prevent contamination of food-to-food and people-to-food.

Single-service utensils and containers have not been constructed to be easily cleanable or sanitized. Bacteria, viruses and food particles would be carried from one customer to the next if these materials were reused. This would result in a very high risk of foodborne illness and possible allergen reactions.

Single-service utensils and containers should:

- Be stored in closed cartons or containers, which protect them from contamination. They must not be placed/stored

under exposed sewer lines or water lines;
- Be dispensed in a manner that prevents contamination of surfaces that come in contact with food or with the mouth of the user; and
- Be disposed of properly, so they do not spread odour and disease or attract pests.

4. Wiping Cloths

MD

4.1 Use wiping cloths in a clean and sanitary manner.

If a server at a busy full-service restaurant uses the same cloth all evening to clean tables, there is a high risk of spreading harmful microorganisms. Each customer that comes in contact with a table surface that has been wiped by a dirty wiping cloth can potentially become ill with foodborne illness.

Wiping cloths used for wiping food spills on food contact surfaces must be:

- Routinely cleaned and, when not in use, kept in a separate sanitizing solution, which is maintained at a concentration as outlined in the Sanitizing Step of Manual Dishwashing found in Section VI.
- Be disposed of properly, so they do not spread odour; and
- Be used for no other purposes, such as wiping raw animal juices.

5. General Premise Housekeeping and Maintenance Schedules

MD

5.1. The areas and surfaces, such as floors, walls and ceilings throughout the foodservice operation, must be cleaned at a frequency that will prevent the accumulation of dust, dirt, food residue and other debris.

Housekeeping and Cleaning

Here are some tips that are important to include in your facility housekeeping and cleaning program:

- Use dry sweeping to clean the floor only under conditions where the food and food contact surfaces will not be contaminated from dust during sweeping.
- Remove dirt or refuse from under fixtures, in corners, and in hard-to-reach places.
- A dust control type vacuum cleaner is the best method of dry cleaning floors.
- Daily cleaning should be done after closing or prior to opening.

Dining/Service Area Cleaning

Ensure that your cleaning program includes:

- Cleaning light fixtures, wall hangings, areas under booth cushions, highchair trays, windows and drapes; and
- Cleaning and sanitizing tables, counters, and other work surfaces.

Section VII
Pest Control

VII - Pest Control

1. Pest Control

1.1 Food must not be contaminated by pests or by microbiological and physical contaminants associated with pests.

Pests such as birds, mice, rats and insects can contaminate food in many ways. They can carry millions of microorganisms that cause foodborne illness. As pests crawl on food and food contact surfaces they leave these microorganisms behind to grow in the food.

Also, insect parts, rodent hair, pest faecal matter and associated debris are physical hazards that are unpleasant and could cause customer distress and shock. At the most extreme levels, these hazards could also cause choking and internal injury.

Insect and Rodent Prevention

The best method of pest control is preventing the entry of the pests into your foodservice operation in the first place. This can be done through the following steps:

- Inspect all incoming food and supplies as they are received and stored. Look in the truck, as it is unloaded. If signs of insects, such as cockroaches, rodents or their droppings are seen, the receiver should closely inspect the boxes and bags of product as it is received. If gross insect or rodent contamination is seen, the entire truck should be rejected and the supplier notified of the problem.
- Monitor storage areas for problems on an ongoing basis, and formally at least every two weeks. Using a flashlight, look for signs of rodent droppings (recent ones will be shiny and soft), footprints in the dust and signs of urine stains. Also look at the base of boxes and bags for signs of rodent gnawing and smear marks from fur. If you find a problem, call your pest control contractor for follow up action.
- Use a "first-in-first-out" inventory control program for food stocks, particularly for cereals and grains. This means that you always use the old product first and the newest product

last. This avoids the problem of having old product sitting around that can be unknowingly infested and an ongoing source of food for pests.

- Keep stored items on shelves or raised skids at least 15 cm (six inches) off the floor.
- Keep storage areas clean. In small storage areas where product is removed from the wall areas weekly, clean storage areas along the wall as they become available. In large storage areas where movement of product might be only monthly, keep shelving two inches from the wall to allow for cleaning and monitoring of the floor to wall junctions. These junctions can be breeding grounds and roadways for rodents and insects.
- Keep pests out of the foodservice operation by making sure that doors and windows are shut or screened. Seal holes in walls, floors or ceilings.
- Remove garbage and unused equipment from food storage areas. This action removes harbourage areas for insects and rodents.

MD 1.2 Food contaminated by pests must be discarded.

Food contaminated by insects, larvae, rodents and/or rodent faecal matter, or birds and/or bird faecal matter, likely contain pathogenic microorganisms and other diseases. The food involved must be discarded.

When pests are found, the following steps must be taken:

- Discard all food that has been contaminated. This food is not fit for human consumption;
- Clean and sanitize the immediate and surrounding areas to prevent further contamination;
- Destroy nesting and breeding places and seal them off to prevent future use; and
- Involve a licensed pest control operator in eradicating uncontrolled insects or rodents. This operator must use approved chemicals. Foodservice operators should not apply insecticides or rodenticides without the appropriate licenses and without consultation with the local public health authority.

7

HR

1.3 Foodservice operators should use certified pest control services to manage the ongoing prevention of pest infestations.

Certified pest control operators are skilled in identifying and eradicating pests. They can provide professional advice on preventing pest infestations and are qualified to handle dangerous pest control chemicals.

When selecting a certified pest control operator, it is important to consider:

- The contractor's experience with other foodservice operations. Be sure to pick someone that has experience with the food industry. They will be more familiar with food pests and their origin;
- The services available. Most pest control companies should be able to provide you with: 1) their list of qualified licensed staff, 2) a listing of the pests covered, 3) frequency of visits, 4) arrangements for additional treatments, 5) emergency response capabilities, and 6) clear reporting procedures;
- The ability of the company to provide a complete service. This includes preventative measures such as the installation, maintenance and cleaning of electronic flying insect killing equipment, as well as advice on good housekeeping, storage and measures to prevent pest entry; and
- The list of chemicals the contractor uses and copies of the written Canadian regulatory approval for the use of these chemicals in food establishments.

A certified pest control operator can use a number of methods to control pests on an ongoing basis. They include:

- Devices that electrocute flying insects. These should be located at least two metres (six feet) away from any food handling areas. This means that these devices should not be located near preparation, cooking, or serving areas. They should also be located away from places where clean utensils, glassware, dishes or pots might be stored;
- Adhesive tapes or traps for insects. These devices should not be located near food products or clean kitchen or service ware;

- Live rodent traps, such as mechanical traps and glue boards. These devices should be checked regularly, at least every week, to remove live and dead rodents. Foodservice operators should monitor their pest control operator to ensure that traps are being checked during regular visits. Traps containing poison should never be located inside a foodservice operation; and
- Application of approved pest control chemicals.

MD

1.4 Rodenticides and insecticides must be applied only by a licensed pest control operator and used in a manner to prevent the contamination of food.

Rodenticides and insecticides are highly toxic and can cause illness and the possibility of death if consumed in food or from affected food contact surfaces. Food preparation, cooking and serving should not be taking place when these chemicals are being applied, and should not resume until they are at safe levels. This may not be possible for 24-hour foodservice operations. In these cases, non-spray methods, such as those outlined above (traps, devices that electrocute, glue boards) should be used. At all times, open food must be protected from contamination.

MD

1.5 Pest control activities must be documented. Foodservice operators must follow up on observations or concerns highlighted by pest control operators.

7

To effectively manage pests in a foodservice operation, it is important to prevent pest entry, eliminate pests when they are found and routinely monitor for signs of pest activity. To show that all efforts have been made to keep pests under control, pest management actions need to be documented. Furthermore, findings of pest control operators, such as recommendations regarding the patching of holes, or application of pesticides to gain control over a growing problem, must be followed up by the foodservice operator. It is the responsibility of the foodservice operator to make sure that an effective pest control program is in place. Documentation is the proof that the program is in place and working.

Documentation

A pest control manual (usually provided by the pest control operator) should outline all the procedures, practices and follow up actions on the pest control program. This manual should include:

- The name of the pest control operator;
- The chemicals used for the pest control program (chemical name, type, concentration and approvals for the chemical);
- The application method of chemicals, name of person applying the chemicals, and where the chemicals were applied;
- Methods of non-chemical control, including maps of the facility (inside and outside) showing the locations of traps, and records showing the results of monitoring them;
- Records of inspection and monitoring (including monitoring done by the foodservice operator and staff); and
- Records outlining the type of follow up taken after the pest control operator made recommendations.

Section VIII
Employee and Visitor Illness, Injury, and Hygiene

VIII - Employee & Visitor Illness, Injury, and Hygiene

1. Illness and Disease

MD

1.1. A foodservice operation must ensure all employees who handle food are free from any symptomatic signs of illness or communicable disease that could be transmitted through food. The foodservice operation must have a program to handle illnesses and communicable diseases.

Employees suffering from a communicable disease are a threat to any Foodservice operation. The ill food handler directly deposits pathogens onto equipment, utensils and other food contact surfaces. Once there, these pathogens can multiply, produce toxins, or infect customers, resulting in foodborne illness.

- Infected employees are the third largest cause of foodborne illnesses in the foodservice industry. If a food handler is directly or indirectly exposed or suffering from a communicable disease, it must be immediately reported to management. For example, a food handler with Hepatitis A, Shigella or E.coli 0157:H7 can easily transfer the disease-causing organisms to food and is considered a severe health hazard to the foodservice operation. Therefore, the foodservice operation must have a program/policy in place where employees are encouraged to report illnesses, particularly those involving digestive upsets and infections, to management.
- The following conditions should be reported to management so that the need for medical examination and possible exclusion from food handling can be considered: jaundice, diarrhea, vomiting, fever, sore throat, visible infection, and discharge from ears, eyes, nose.
- If a physician diagnoses an employee with a communicable disease, the incident must be reported to the local health department.
- Employees must obtain written clearance from the treating physician (especially in the case of diagnosed, reportable communicable disease) before returning to work after medical leave or illness.

- The manager or owner/operator must instruct employees suffering from a temporary illness (i.e. sore throat, cough, sinus pain/infection or other symptoms of a cold and/or flu) not to work in contact with food or food contact surfaces. If the nature of the illness allows, the employee could be reassigned to work in another area that will not result in contamination of the food.

2. Injuries

MD

2.1 Employees with open/exposed wounds must not participate in food handling activities.

Food handlers working with cuts, burns, boils, open sores and wounds are a health hazard to the foodservice operation. For example, an employee with an open wound containing pus that is exposed and draining can be a source of Staphylococcus aureus. This pathogen can easily be transmitted to food and food contact surfaces, increasing the risk of foodborne illness.

Steps to take if an employee has a cut, burn, boil, sore, skin infection or infected wound:

- If the employee obtained the injury at the foodservice operation the immediate area must be cleaned and sanitized and any food contacted must be disposed of immediately;
- The food handler should be removed from food handling activities entirely; or
- The injury should be bandaged with a clean, dry and tight fitting (wound leakage protection) covering/bandage. A waterproof, disposable plastic glove must be worn over the bandage. Employees wearing bandages may need to be moved to tasks away from the direct handling of food and food contact surfaces.

8

3. Employee Hygiene

MD

3.1 Employees must be aware and follow good hygiene practices set by the establishment.

The cleanliness and personal hygiene of food handlers is extremely important to the overall sanitary environment of the foodservice operation. Good personal hygiene is a critical protective measure against foodborne illness and customers expect it. If a food handler is not practicing good personal hygiene, the food, food contact surfaces and the premises may become contaminated. For example, all humans can serve as the host or carrier for disease-causing organisms. These organisms are frequently present on hands; faces, in the hair and mouths, noses and intestinal tract of humans. Therefore, good personal hygiene is essential for food handlers in order to decrease the risk of contamination through food, food contact surfaces (i.e. dishes, utensils) and the premises.

By establishing a personal hygiene program that includes specific policies and by training and enforcing those policies, a foodservice operation can minimize the risk of causing foodborne illness and lost business.

MD

3.2 All food preparation personnel must wear clean outer clothing. Aprons must be changed when a food handler moves from raw to ready-to-eat food preparation.

Employee uniforms can be a source of pathogenic bacteria and viruses. These microorganisms can be transferred to food and food contact surfaces through direct contact with clothing or indirect through hands, utensils, or equipment. Clean clothing minimizes the risk of cross contamination.

- Food handlers in food preparation areas must wear clean outer clothing. Protective clothing such as aprons and working clothing must be clean, comfortable, and of a material suited to the purpose, and clothing must be laundered daily.
- Uniforms should be changed when they become contaminated. The wearing of street clothes in food handling areas should be discouraged. Working attire should not be worn outside of the foodservice operation (i.e. on public transportation to and from work). Sweaters should not be worn over a working uniform unless they are a part of the uniform.

- Shoes should be clean, non-slip, and be worn only in the foodservice operation. Shoes that have been worn on a farm or in other conditions could result in cross-contamination.

HR

3.3. Personnel in food preparation areas should wear a hair restraint. Where required, beard nets should also be worn.

Hairs on your head and face contain millions of bacteria. Some of these bacteria could cause food poisoning.

- Employees and any person entering a food preparation or storage area should wear hair restraints such as clean hats or hairnets. If necessary, beards should also be covered with beard nets. Hair and/or beard restraints discourage food handlers from touching their hair or beards. The restraints also prevent hair from falling onto the food or food contact surfaces.
- Food handlers must wear the appropriate hair/beard restraints to completely cover all of the hair.

MD

3.4 Food handlers must avoid behaviors that could result in food contamination (i.e. smoking).

Bacteria and viruses can be carried on cigarettes, dirty tissue, and food containers such as juice and water bottles. In addition, false fingernails, nail polish, and false eyelashes can transport microorganisms as well as cause a physical hazard in foods. Using these objects during the preparation of food can lead to customer injury and illness.

- Food handlers must refrain from behaviour that could result in food contamination. The following activities are prohibited during food handling, preparation, service, and cleaning: eating and drinking; smoking; spitting; chewing gum; blowing nose; sneezing and coughing onto foods/food contact surfaces. If sneezing and coughing are unavoidable, direct the sneeze or cough into the bend of your elbow and always away from the food.
- Food handlers should not wear any nail polish or false nails.

8

The nail polish or nail could chip or break off into the food product. This would be considered a contaminant as well as a physical hazard.
* Good hygiene habits including bathing and washing hair on a daily basis.

HR

3.5. Jewelry should be removed before working with food.

Jewelry, generally speaking is difficult to keep clean. For example, bacteria can harbour between the skin and the piece of jewelry or between the stone/setting in a ring and then be transferred into the food product. Jewelry is also a danger as it could accidentally fall into the food and become a choking hazard, or become caught on a piece of equipment and become an occupational hazard.

* For everyone's safety, a "no jewelry" policy should be enforced.
* Only medical alert bracelets or necklaces are permitted and should be worn underneath clothing to prevent them from falling into food products.

MD

3.6 Employees must strictly follow handwashing and disposable glove procedures.
See Section III – Construction, for handwashing station and supplies requirements.

Bacteria and other contaminants are present on hands, especially on the fingertips and under the nail beds. While handwashing may appear as common sense, many food handlers fail to wash their hands thoroughly and as often as needed. If hands are not properly and often washed, there is an increased risk of contamination to the food and food contact surfaces.

Employees involved in food preparation and foodservice must thoroughly understand when and how to wash their hands.

Handwashing (Eight-Step Procedure):

- *To ensure proper handwashing by food handlers, the following steps must be practiced:*
  1) Wet hands and exposed arms (at least up to the wrists) with warm running water;
  2) Apply liquid soap;
  3) Vigorously rub together the surfaces of liquid soap, lathered hands and exposed arms for at least 20 seconds;
  4) Use a brush under the fingernails and other very dirty areas;
  5) Follow with a thorough rinsing with clean, warm water (wrists pointed downwards);
  6) Soap and lather vigorously again;
  7) Rinse hand and wrists thoroughly; and
  8) Dry hands with a single-use paper towel. Use paper towel to turn off the tap (if not using a foot-controlled tap activation).

Note: Never dry hands on apron or dishtowel, as this would re-contaminate hands.

In addition to proper handwashing, fingernails should be trimmed, filed and maintained short so that proper handwashing will effectively remove soil from under and around them.

8

Correct Hand Washing Procedure

1 Wet Hands

2 Soap

3 Lather

4 Brush

5 Rinse

6 Soap-Lather

7 Rinse

8 Towel Dry

Employees must always wash hands and arms prior to starting work, frequently during their shift, and definitely after:

a) Using the toilet facilities;
b) A meal/drink break;
c) Coughing;
d) Sneezing or blowing the nose;
e) Handling raw foods;
f) Smoking;
g) Handling money;
h) Before and after handling potentially hazardous foods; and
i) Changing work stations from raw food preparation activities to ready-to-eat activities.

Disposable Gloves

- When a foodservice operation requires food handlers to use disposable gloves, regular glove changes, as well as proper hand and glove washing, is essential. Touching dirty surfaces can contaminate gloves. If gloves become contaminated, they must be changed. Gloves should be treated like a second skin, but must be regularly replaced. Gloves must be changed regularly throughout the day; when they become ripped or worn; or when there is a change in activity between handling cooked and raw products. Gloves should be made of materials that are impermeable to water. Plastic and vinyl disposable gloves are most common. Latex gloves are not recommended because some customers and employees can have highly allergic reactions to latex residues from gloves left on food and food contact surfaces.

Procedures for gloves include that:

- Employees must wash their hands (using the previously mentioned procedure) before putting on disposable gloves.
- Gloves must be discarded after each use and/or after four hours of continuous use performing the same task provided there has been no contamination.
- Gloves should be changed if they become torn or after any action that might cause contamination such as picking up an item from the floor.

8

- New gloves are worn after breaks, meals or visits to the washroom.
- Employees involved in food preparation and foodservice must thoroughly understand when and how exactly to wash their hands.

A Case in Point

A food handler is in charge of all the cold salad preparation at a hotel restaurant. This includes physical hand mixing of green salads for the evening meals. The food manager on duty noticed an open wound on the right-hand of the employee, while the employee sneezed into her hand.

The Problem:
These actions by the food handler could easily contaminate the food and surrounding food contact surfaces.

Solution:
Due to her injury and possible illness, this food handler should not be handling food under any circumstances. The manager should remove the employee from direct food handling tasks, bandage and glove the wound and have the employee work in low risk, non-food contact areas.

---

4. Visitors Policy

4.1 All visitors, including delivery and repair personnel to a food preparation area should observe the same hygiene and dress code as food handlers working in the foodservice operation.

Visitors such as salespeople and delivery personnel are considered potential risks of contamination to the foodservice operation. Their clothing/apparel and hair may have contaminants that could be transferred to food, food contact surfaces and/or the premise.

Therefore, the foodservice operation must enforce the personal hygiene policy for all visitors including handwashing and hair restraint policies.

- Visitors should practice good personal hygiene by wearing clean, protective clothing provided by the foodservice operation including, hair restraints and/or outer protective coats.
- Visitors should refrain from coming into close proximity or contact with food and food equipment, and from any activities that could contaminate food.

8

Section IX
Education and Training

IX - Education and Training

1. Operator Training

MD

Every foodservice operator must hold a certificate confirming his or her successful completion of a food handler training program recognized by the regulatory authority. When this operator is absent from the premises, at least one other person at the facility must hold a recognized food safety certificate.

Training is very important to food safety in a foodservice operation. If food handlers are unaware of ways food can become contaminated, then the entire foodservice operation and its customers are at risk. For example, the majority of all foodborne illnesses can be traced to the actions of food handlers who either did not know or understand the value of using designated food safety procedures. In the absence of the foodservice operator, at least one other employee must have recognized food safety certification, to ensure the consistent application of food safety practices. Ultimately all employees (at every level) should be familiar with their role and responsibility in protecting food from contamination.

Operator Training:

The following knowledge and skills must be learned during operator training:

a) The importance of and the relationship between foodborne illness prevention and employee personal hygiene;
b) How to handle employees with disease or medical conditions who may transmit foodborne diseases;
c) The importance of time/temperature when handling potentially hazardous food;
d) The hazards related to the consumption of raw or undercooked meat, poultry, eggs, fish, fruits, and vegetables;
e) The importance and the requirements of time/temperature when cooking potentially hazardous food such as meats, poultry, eggs and fish;
f) The requirements of time/temperature for hot holding, cooling, cooking, safe refrigerated storage, and reheating of potentially hazardous food;

g) The relationship between foodborne illness and managing: cross-contamination, ready-to-eat foods, hand washing, personal hygiene, and premises cleaning;

h) The relationship between food safety and equipment design, installation, capacity, maintenance and cleaning;

i) Correct procedures for cleaning and sanitizing utensils and food contact surfaces of equipment;

j) Knowledge of the sources of water used in the foodservice operation and procedures taken to ensure it is protected from contamination, such as providing protection from backflow and cross-connections;

k) The correct handling procedures of poisonous or toxic chemicals and allergens in the foodservice operation and the procedures for safely storing, dispensing and using these chemicals or allergens;

l) Knowledge of critical control points (CCPs) and the ability to explain steps taken to ensure that the points are controlled in accordance with the regulatory authority; and;

m) Understanding the responsibilities, rights and authorities assigned by local laws or the appropriate Code (Provincial and/or Federal) as it applies to either the food employee (i.e. the food handler), the person in charge (i.e. the manager/supervisor), and regulatory authority (i.e. the health/building/fire inspector).

Food Training Programs:

There are two levels of food handler training programs for foodservice operations. These levels are: food handler training and operator training. For details on various certification courses contact the Canadian Restaurant and Foodservices Association (CRFA) and/or your local health department.

- Certification resulting from training courses should be valid for five years after completion of the course. After five years, operators or food handlers may be required to participate in a refresher or updating course.
- The regulatory authority having jurisdiction must recognize food handler training programs based on national standards.
- The training of operators or food handlers can be undertaken by a third party that is authorized by the

9

regulatory agency (contact your local regulatory agency for details).

1. Employee Training

Employees in foodservice operations must have the necessary skills and knowledge to handle food hygienically.

Employees who come into direct contact with food should be trained in food safety and food hygiene to a level appropriate to the operations they are required to perform. Training is essential for a safe food environment. Remember, most of the problems related to foodborne illness are due to food handler error and improper time/temperature management, personal hygiene and health, and cross-contamination.

Food Handler Training:

Food handlers must have the necessary knowledge and skills to enable them to handle food safely. Foodservice operators must ensure ongoing food safety education is available for their food handlers through activities as information updates, classroom instruction, on-the-job training, and formal food safety certification and employee meetings. Tools that support the ongoing education of employees such as posters and videos can also be used. A foodservice operator should evaluate a food handler's food safety performance continuously and, formally, at least once a year.

Educational courses and programs provided to food handlers should be designed to meet or exceed the following learning objectives set by the FRFS Code. The learners should have knowledge of the:
- Food handler's role and responsibility in protecting food from contamination and deterioration;
- Main properties of common foods (i.e. colour, texture, odour);
- Main types of microorganisms, their sources, the physical and chemical factors that affect their growth, reproduction, activity and death, and the difference between harmful and harmless microorganisms;

- Common causes of foodborne illnesses, their characteristics and the procedures and practices that will prevent and control their incidence;
- Basic elements of HACCP; and
- Allergenic properties of certain foods.

In an effort to keep track of which food handlers have been trained through a food safety certification course, the operator should maintain records of which employees have taken courses, the dates, and any additional relevant information. There are two options for documenting this type of information:

a) Keep a copy of the original certificate in the employee's personnel file; or

b) Copy the attendance list for the course date, and keep it in a master employee training file.

Section X
Food Safety Program
Management

X - Food Safety Program Management

1. Supervision and Food Safety Program

MD

1.1. The foodservice operation must ensure that there is a food safety program in place and working to effectively control and handle potential food contamination.

In a foodservice operation, the potential for biological, chemical and physical hazards will vary from one product to another. Foodservice operators need to determine the steps in each operation that require effective controls to eliminate hazards or to minimize risk. Not all foodservice operations can apply one particular food safety program. Therefore, it is necessary for the owner/operator to determine what type of risk-based food safety program will be used to control food related risks and minimize the potential of foodborne illness outbreaks.

A Hazard Analysis Critical Control Point (HACCP) food safety system is an internationally proven, risk-based program. This is a gold standard in the world for managing food safety hazards. See Appendix A – Introduction to HACCP.

There are many different types of foodservice operations such as quick service, full service and catering. Not all foodservice operations can adhere to one particular food safety program. It is important for the foodservice operation to; analyze the public health risks of the foods being served; analyze the operation's customers or clientele being served; and determine if they are a high risk group (i.e. young children or elderly). The foodservice operation should develop and implement a food safety program that addresses the relevant food safety concerns (i.e. chemical, physical, biological, or allergen).

For the food safety program to be complete it must include three levels of activity:

1 **Procedures**
   A written version of the food safety program, explaining what and how tasks are to be performed in order to provide a safe food product.

2. **Records**

   Record forms are provided for the employees to use. These forms are completed as the tasks are performed. They are proof that activities were done as indicated by the procedures.

3. **Activities**

   Employees are to be trained as per the written procedures and function accordingly in order to prevent food contamination.

Record Keeping

The following are examples of records that the foodservice operation should keep and have available for review for at least three months:

1.1. Employee food safety training (i.e. records should include date and content of food safety certification course completed);

1.2. Cleaning and sanitation (i.e. records should include date and time cleaning and sanitation of employee restrooms);

1.3. Temperature control (i.e. refrigerated storage temperature logs); and

1.4. Pest control operator report.

1.5. Incoming material/receiving report.

HR

   1.2. Well-trained and knowledgeable supervisory staff needs to be available and accessible during all hours of operation to respond to various food hazard concerns and, if necessary, apply corrective actions.

The effectiveness of any food safety program is only as good as the foodservice operation's capacity to carry it out. It is essential that knowledgeable supervisory staff be able to manage, prevent, react to, and correct any food hazard concerns.

In a foodservice operation, there should be direction from the management to provide effective supervision to ensure a safe food environment. A trained supervisor should:

10

- Be accessible at all times during foodservice operations;
- Understand how to implement safe food practices, address potential food risks and take corrective actions when necessary; and
- Refer to the Education and Training Section in this Code of Practice for training requirements.

Appendices

Appendix A

Introduction to HACCP (Hazard Analysis and Critical Control Points)

What is HACCP?

HACCP (pronounced ha-sip) stands for Hazard Analysis and Critical Control Points. HACCP is a way of preventing biological, chemical and physical hazards in food. The HACCP approach is a new way of ensuring the safety of food. In the past, food safety was managed by conducting finished product testing and inspection of food facilities. This approach was badly timed, expensive, and inaccurate. By the time that products were identified as unsafe, they often had already been packaged, and in some cases, distributed to customers.

HACCP is aimed at identifying and correcting possible food safety risks before they happen. HACCP is a recognized, proven system that has been adapted for use in foodservice operations. Across Canada HACCP is being implemented on the farm, in food processing plants, in food distribution centers and in retail food stores.

How do you Implement HACCP?

A HACCP program is applied to a foodservice operation by:

1. Analyzing your process/menu items from start (receiving of ingredients) to finish (serving the food) and determining where significant hazards are likely to occur;
2. Establishing which hazards are controlled by your Good Operational Practices and putting special requirements in place to monitor and manage the remaining key hazards;
3. Having someone review that all the required "checks" are being done and are effective; and
4. Keeping records and written procedures so that food safety is managed the same way by everyone.

HACCP may seem complicated; however, it is an effective, common sense approach to keeping food safe. Most foodservice operations are already doing many of the activities necessary to keep food safe. HACCP goes one step further: it helps you to anticipate potential problems and prevent them from occurring. HACCP protects your business by managing biological, chemical (including allergens) and physical hazards.

A Case in Point

In 1992-93, four children died and over 500 children and adults were stricken with food poisoning from E. coli 0157:H7. The most identified food source was undercooked hamburger patties sold through the Jack-in-the-Box restaurant chain in the U.S.

The Problem:
The incoming hamburger was infected with a dangerous pathogen. Jack-in-the-Box did not anticipate this possibility and did not put measures in place to manage this risk. Some of the Jack-in-the-Box stores were undercooking the hamburgers in violation of the law in many jurisdictions. This was not unusual for many restaurateurs who believed that an undercooked hamburger had a better taste. This practice has all but disappeared today.

Solution:
The incident emphasized that hamburgers and other high-risk foods should be cooked to an adequate temperature to destroy dangerous microorganisms. It was the first time that HACCP-based systems were considered essential from the farm to food service. Today Jack-in-the-Box has one of the food service industry's most progressive HACCP programs.

The Six Preparation Steps and Seven Principles of HACCP:

The following steps provide you with a brief overview of HACCP implementation. The CRFA has developed a detailed set of tools available to assist foodservice operators in implementing a HACCP-based plan. Contact the Canadian Restaurant and Foodservice Association for its "Food Safety Essentials".

Six Steps of a HACCP Plan

1. Assemble the HACCP team: This group of people will provide you with the details on how your facility operates from preparation to serving;
2. Develop Good Operating Practices: This step requires that you ensure that you have simple documented procedures on: Facilities, Receiving and Storage, Equipment, Personnel, Sanitation, Pest Control and Traceability;
3. Describe your menu categories: This step helps to simplify your HACCP programs by grouping similar menu items and reducing the number of HACCP plans;
4. Identify all your incoming ingredients and materials: This list will help you to conduct your hazard analysis and identify products that might have hidden hazards such as allergens;
5. Construct your flow diagrams: These diagrams describe the step-by-step process of preparing a certain group of menu items, for example casseroles; and
6. Construct your foodservice operation floor plan: This floor plan helps to identify potential hazards associated with the flow of food, people and equipment in your foodservice operation.

Seven Principles of a HACCP Plan

Once the six preparation steps are completed, then a foodservice operator can develop a HACCP plan. There are seven principles in the development of each HACCP plan. One HACCP plan will be required for each grouping of menu items. A foodservice operation may have as few as one or as many as 10 HACCP plans.

1. Hazard Analysis
The foodservice operator lists all the possible biological, chemical (including allergens) and physical hazards associated with the ingredients and process steps in a group of menu items.

2. Determine Critical Control Points (CCP)
Once you have identified all potential food hazards and the step or steps at which they occur in your establishment, the next task

is determining at which steps we can intervene to control these hazards. Some of the hazards will be controlled by your good operational practices, for example: storage temperatures.

However, other hazards can only be controlled at a specific point in the process of making that product. A CCP is defined as a point, step or procedure where control can be applied and the hazard can be prevented, eliminated, or reduced to an acceptable level. In essence, if we lose control at this point, someone could get sick. Critical control points are based on criteria such as cook time and temperature.

3. Establish Critical Limits
Once you have determined the critical points of control CCPs for a specific group of menu items, you need to establish critical limits. Critical limits are minimum and maximum limits that the critical control point must meet in order to prevent, eliminate, or reduce a hazard to an acceptable limit. The critical limits must be measurable (such as time and temperature). They must also be based on scientific data, food regulations (such as the Food Retail and Foodservices Code), and expert advice.

4. Monitoring
Monitoring lets you know that critical limits are being met, and that you are doing things right. To develop a successful monitoring program, you need to focus on:
* Who will monitor;
* How to monitor;
* When to monitor; and
* Where to monitor.

Monitoring techniques should be explained in detail, measurable and clear.

5. Taking Corrective Actions
Corrective actions are predetermined steps taken when food does not meet a critical limit as noted in the monitoring procedure. Remember, this will be the last opportunity you have to ensure the safety of the food served. The corrective action tells employees what to do if the product does not meet the predetermined food safety requirements.

6. Verification (Verify that the System Works)

After you have developed your system you need to confirm that it works according to the plan. This is called verification. Verification of your plan should be performed on a regular basis. This is sometimes done by reviewing records, watching people perform critical control point checks, or through things like microbiological analysis.

7. Record Keeping (Documentation)

Recording how food is produced and kept safe is important to the success of a HACCP system. Proper records allow you to document that you are continuously preparing and serving safe food. Also, record keeping allows you to analyze problems and make changes to prevent similar situations in the future.

What is the key to successful HACCP Implementation?

People are the key to successful HACCP implementation. The only way for this system to effectively prevent foodborne illness is for all personnel to understand, accept and carry out the requirements of the HACCP program on a daily basis. Management's support and commitment is essential. A HACCP program can be the most cost-effective method of maximizing menu item safety. However, the program is only as good as the people behind it.

Note: For more information on Canada's HACCP Program for food manufacturers, the Food Safety Enhancement Program, go to www.inspection.gc.ca

Appendix B

"Boil Water" Advisory
(Reference- Ontario Ministry of Health and Long-Term Care)
www.gov.on.ca

What are the reasons for a "boil water" advisory?

A "boil water" advisory may be issued as a result of any of the following:

1) A bacteriological (microbial) examination, including the finding of bacteria or parasites within the water source;
2) Information other than bacteriological examination indicating that the water is not safe-to-drink (i.e. lack or absence of disinfection residual in the drinking water);
3) Following the occurrence of an outbreak of illness within the community that has been linked to the consumption of the drinking water.

The extent of restriction on water use depends on the situation and the reason for issuing a boil water advisory. Always, follow the local health authorities' recommendations on water use.

Simple procedure for boiling water:

1) Put water in clean and sanitized, heat resistant pot/container;
2) Put heat resistant pot containing water on stove burner;
3) Heat water until it is brought to a rapid rolling boil;
4) Continue rolling boil for at least five minutes;
5) After five minutes, if necessary, cool water by placing it in another sanitized container and store in the refrigerator.

How do I use water when a "boil water" advisory has been issued?

In a foodservice operation, the following list outlines how the boiled water should be used:

1) All water used as an ingredient in any food products (i.e. salads, soups, beverages and desserts, etc.);
2) All water used to wash or rinse food products;
3) All water used for drinking;
4) All water added to drinks such as tea/coffee/soda/carbonated beverage machines (This applies to pop dispenser nozzles in bar facilities).
5) All water used to make consumable ice or ice products (It may be preferable to purchase commercially bagged ice from an approved source/supplier).
6) All water used for handwashing. A bottled water product should be used if more convenient.
7) If heat (hot water) is used as the sanitizing method for dishes, equipment and utensils, operators must ensure the final rinse temperature of the mechanical dishwashing machine reaches 82°C (180°F). Otherwise, you can fill the third compartment of a three-compartment sink (manual-dishwashing option) with the boiled water and add a sufficient amount of an approved chemical as the sanitization process (contact local health authorities).

Appendix C

Thermometer Calibration

Thermometers should be calibrated using either the ice-point or boiling-point method outlined below. The ice-point method is most commonly used unless a thermometer is not capable of registering a temperature of 32°F (0°C).

Note: The boiling-point method is sometimes less reliable due to variations in altitude and atmospheric pressure.

Ice-Point Method:

1. Fill a large glass with crushed ice. Add enough clean tap water until the glass is full. Stir the mixture well to mix the ice with the water to form an ice-water slurry solution.

2. Put the thermometer or probe stem into the ice water so that the sensing area (the immersion area below the dimple) is completely submerged. Wait at least 30 seconds (Note: Do not let the stem touch the bottom or sides of the glass. The thermometer stem or probe stem must remain in the ice water).

3. Hold the adjusting nut securely with a wrench or other tool and rotate the head of the thermometer until it reads 0°C (32°F). If using a digital thermometer, press the reset button on the digital thermometer to adjust the readout.

Boiling-Point Method:

1. Bring clean tap water to a boil in a deep pot/pan.

2. Put the thermometer or probe stem into the boiling water so that the sensing area (the immersion area below the dimple) is completely submerged. Wait at least 30 seconds (Note: Do not let the stem touch the bottom or sides of the pot/pan. The thermometer stem or probe stem must remain in the boiling water).

3. Hold the adjusting nut securely with a wrench or other tool and rotate the head of the thermometer until it reads 212°F (100°C) or the appropriate boiling temperature. If using a digital thermometer, press the reset button on the digital thermometer to adjust the readout (Note: The boiling point of water is about 1°F (about 0.5°C) lower for every 550 feet (168m) you are above sea level).

TEMPERATURE DANGER ZONE FOR FOOD

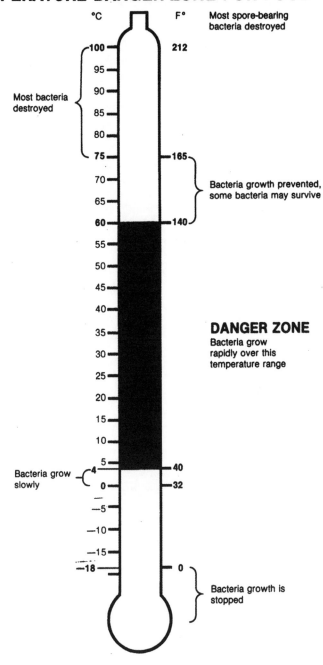

CONVERSION SCALES

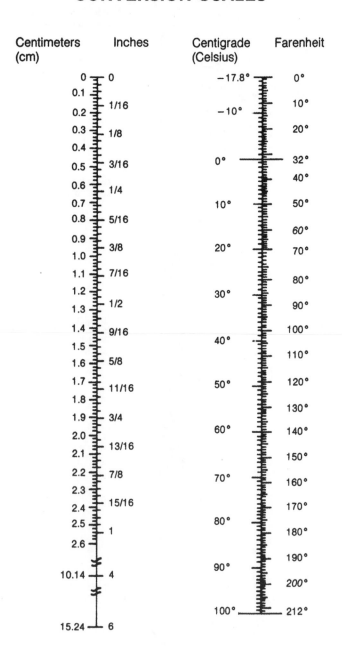

Centimeters (cm)	Inches		Centigrade (Celsius)	Farenheit
0	0		−17.8°	0°
0.1				10°
0.2	1/16		−10°	
0.3	1/8			20°
0.4				
0.5	3/16		0°	32°
0.6	1/4			40°
0.7			10°	50°
0.8	5/16			
0.9	3/8		20°	60°
1.0				70°
1.1	7/16			80°
1.2			30°	
1.3	1/2			90°
1.4	9/16			100°
1.5			40°	
1.6	5/8			110°
1.7	11/16		50°	120°
1.8				130°
1.9	3/4		60°	140°
2.0	13/16			150°
2.1				
2.2	7/8		70°	160°
2.3	15/16			170°
2.4			80°	
2.5	1			180°
2.6				190°
10.14	4		90°	200°
15.24	6		100°	212°

Appendix F

How to Respond to Suspected Foodborne Illness

Product complaints are an important indicator of possible deficiencies of manufacturing controls and /or the distribution handling system. Deficiencies in the complaint handling system could result in failure to identify and eliminate health risks.

Customers sometimes complain that they have become ill from eating food in foodservice operations. In order to protect your operation, it is important to take these complaints seriously. Your operation may or may not be responsible for the illness. Taking steps to investigate the cause shows that you care about the customer. It also establishes "due diligence", which means that you have taken reasonable care to prevent future problems and/or determined that your operation is not responsible.

For the protection of the public and health of customers, it is necessary that any complaints of suspected foodborne illness be investigated immediately. Time is everything in determining the cause of foodborne illness. When a case of food poisoning is reported, the following steps are suggested:

a) An identified individual will receive, evaluate, categorize, and investigate complaints. It is best if a standardized form is available. If a form is not available, be sure to include the following information:
   - Name, address and telephone number of complainant.
   - If it is a food quality or food safety issue.
   - List of all the foods that were consumed.
   - Date that the food was consumed.
   - Time between purchase of food and consumption.
   - Time between food consumed and when symptoms of illness commenced.
   - Symptoms of the illness.
   - Determine whether a doctor confirmed the illness. Was food poisoning diagnosed and confirmed by a doctor? If yes, what pathogen was involved?
   - Determine whether the public health authorities are currently involved.

b) If the public health authorities have not been involved, you can notify public health authorities or you can suggest that the customer notify the authorities. The source of the problem may not be your operation, so it is important for the authorities to take a full history of the complaint from the customer. This will help to identify other possible causes of the problem. It may also require the customer to get a medical diagnosis if one has not already been done.

c) Investigate the complaint. Determine which foods may have been involved. Determine which staff might be involved (it might not be the food, but a human carrier of the pathogen). If any of the suspected food remains, remove the food from service and label it clearly so it does not end up back in production. Keep it refrigerated and covered for testing by the health authorities. Check to see if other complaints of this nature have been received. Are similar foods implicated?

d) Work with health authorities to determine if your suppliers have received other complaints about their products.

e) Keep records of the outcome of the investigation and what changes were made, if any, to your operation. It is best to keep these records for a minimum of two years.

f) Periodically check to determine if there are any patterns to the complaints you receive. If there are patterns, determine what should be done to prevent future illnesses and make changes. Keep records of your analysis and any improvements you made to your operation (i.e. refresher training for staff).

For a complete and detailed procedure with flow diagrams and forms, refer to the procedures and steps outlined in the **Canadian Restaurant and Foodservices Association Foodservice Establishment Distributor/Supplier Product Recall and Consumer Menu Item Complaint Plan (available from CRFA).**

Appendix G

How to Respond to a Supplier Recall

You may hear about a recall on your supplier's products from a number of sources - the supplier, through the media or through health authorities. Your supplier or health authority may instruct you on what to do with the product. If not, you may take the following steps:

a) Determine the amount of the recalled product you have on hand by noting the product code, size and name. Check product salad bars, display areas, refrigerator and other holding areas where the product might be located.

b) Remove, wrap (if currently unwrapped) and box up the affected product. Tape the box or container closed and label it with the words "Recalled Product – Do Not Use."

c) Notify supplier of the amount of recalled product you have on hand and ask for instructions on its disposal. You might be instructed to return it on the next truck, hold it for pick up or throw it out.

d) Keep accurate records of the reason for the recall, amount of product recalled, code and type of product.

For detailed procedures on product recalls follow the procedures and steps outlined in the **Canadian Restaurant and Foodservices Association Foodservice Establishment Distributor/Supplier Product Recall and Consumer Menu Item Complaint Plan** (available from CRFA).

Major Foodborne Illnesses

DISEASE	Salmonellosis	Shigellosis
PATHOGEN	Salmonella	Shigella
INCUBATION PERIOD	6 – 48 hours	12 – 50 hours
DURATION OF ILLNESS	1 –2 days (may last longer)	Indefinite, depends on treatment
SYMPTOMS	Abdominal pain, headache, nausea, vomiting, fever, diarrhea	Diarrhea (sometimes bloody), abdominal pain, fever, vomiting, chills, lassitude, dehydration
SOURCE	Domestic and wild animals, humans (intestinal tract) – especially as carriers	Humans (intestinal tract), flies
FOODS INVOLVED	Poultry and poultry salads, meat and meat products, fish, shrimp, sliced melons, sliced tomatoes, milk, shell eggs, egg custards and sauces, and other protein foods	Salads (potato, tuna, shrimp, chicken, and macaroni), lettuce, raw vegetables, milk and dairy products, poultry, moist and mixed foods
PREVENTION	Avoid cross-contamination, refrigerate food, thoroughly cook poultry to at least 85°C (185°F) for 15 seconds, rapidly cool cooked meats and meat products, avoid contamination from foodservice employees by practicing good personal hygiene	Avoid cross-contamination, avoid fecal contamination from foodservice employees by practicing good personal hygiene, use sanitary food and water sources, control flies, rapidly cool foods

Listeriosis	Staphylococcus	Clostridium Perfringens
Listeria monocytogenes	Staphylococcus aureus	Enteritis Clostridium perfringens
2-3 days – 3 weeks	Rapid	8 –22 hours
Indefinite, depends on treatment; high fatality rates in immuno-compromised individuals	2 –3 days	24 hours (may last 1 –2 weeks
Nausea, vomiting, diarrhea, headache, persistent fever, chills, backache, meningitis	Nausea, vomiting, abdominal cramps; in more severe cases, headache, muscle cramping, changes in blood pressure and pulse rate	Abdominal pain, diarrhea, dehydration
Soil, water, mud, humans, domestic and wild animals, fowl, damp environments	Humans (skin, hair, nose, throat, infected sores), animals	Humans (intestinal tract), animals, soil
Unpasteurized milk and cheese, ice cream, raw vegetables, poultry and meats, seafood, and prepared, chilled, ready-to-eat foods	Ham and other meats, poultry, warmed-over foods, egg products, milk and dairy products, custards, potato salads, cream-filled pastries, and other protein foods	Cooked meat, meat products, poultry, gravy, beans that have been cooled slowly
Use only pasteurized milk and dairy products, cook foods to proper internal temperatures, avoid cross-contamination, clean and sanitize surfaces, avoid pooling water	Avoid cross-contamination from bare hands, practice good personal hygiene, exclude foodservice employees with skin infections from food preparation, properly refrigerate food, rapidly cool prepared foods	Use careful time and temperature control in cooling and reheating cooked meat, poultry, and bean dishes and products to 74°C (165°F) for at least 15 seconds within two hours

Major Foodborne Illnesses

DISEASE	Bacillus Cereus Gastroenteritis	Botulism
PATHOGEN	Bacillus cereus	Clostridium botulinum
INCUBATION PERIOD	$^1/_2$ - 6 hours (emetic type); 6 – 15 hours (diarrheal type)	18 – 36 hours (may vary from 4 hours – 8 days)
DURATION OF ILLNESS	Less than 24 hours (emetic); 24 hours (diarrheal)	Several days – a year
SYMPTOMS	Nausea and vomiting, occasional abdominal cramps and/or diarrhea, abdominal cramps, pain, nausea (diarrheal)	Lassitude, weakness, vertigo, double vision, difficulty speaking and swallowing, constipation
SOURCE	Soil, dust	Soil, water
FOODS INVOLVED	Rice products, starchy foods (potato, pasta, and cheese products), sauces, puddings, soups, casseroles, pastries, salads (emetic); meats, milk, vegetables, fish (diarrheal)	Improperly processing canned low acid foods, garlic-in-oil products, grilled sautéed onions in butter sauce, leftover baked potatoes, stews, meat/poultry loaves
PREVENTION	Use careful time and temperature control and quick-chilling methods to cool foods, hold hot foods at 60°C (140°F) or higher, reheat leftovers to 74°C (165°F) for at least 15 seconds within 2 hours	Do not use home-canned products, use careful time and temperature control for sours vide items and all large, bulky foods, purchase garlic and oil mixtures in small quantities for immediate use and keep refrigerated, cook sautéed onions on request, rapidly cool leftovers

Campylobacteriosis	E. coli O 157: H7 Enteritis	Norwalk Virus Gastroenteritis
Campylobacter jejuni	Escherichia coli	Norwalk and Norwalk-like viral agent
2 –5 days	2 – 9 days	24 – 48 hours
7 –10 days (relapses common)	8 days	24 – 60 hours
Diarrhea (watery or bloody), fever, nausea, abdominal pain, nausea, headache, muscle pain	Diarrhea (watery, could become bloody), severe abdominal cramps and pain, vomiting, occasional low-grade fever	Nausea, vomiting, diarrhea, abdominal pain, headache, low-grade fever
Domestic and wild animals (intestinal tract)	Animals, particularly cattle, humans (intestinal tract)	Humans (intestinal tract)
Unpasteurized milk and dairy products, poultry, pork, beef, lamb, non-chlorinated water	Raw and undercooked ground beef, imported cheeses, unpasteurized milk, roast beef, dry salami, apple cider, commercial mayonnaise	Raw shellfish, raw vegetables, salads, prepared salads, water contaminated from human feces
Thoroughly cook food to minimum safe internal temperatures, avoid cross-contamination	Thoroughly cook ground beef to at least 70°C (158°F) for 15 seconds, avoid cross-contamination from foodservice employees by practicing good personal hygiene	Obtain shellfish from approved, certified sources, avoid fecal contamination from foodservice employees by practicing good personal hygiene, thoroughly cook foods to minimum safe internal temperatures, use chlorinated water

Helpful Contact Information

Federal Departments

Canada Food and Drugs Act:
Phone: (613) 957-4222
http://lois.justice.gc.ca/en/F-27/

Consumer Packaging and Labelling Act:
Phone: (613) 957-4222
http://lois.justice.gc.ca/en/C-38

Canada Meat Inspection Act:
Phone: (613) 957-4222
http://lois.justice.gc.ca/en/M-3.2/76171.html

Canada Agriculture Products:
Phone: (613) 957-4222
http://lois.justice.gc.ca/en/C-0.4/9473.html

Canada Fish Inspection Act:
Phone: (613) 957-4222
http://lois.justice.gc.ca/en/F-12/

WHMIS information:
www.msdssearch.com

For further information on **National Building Code, National Fire Code, National Plumbing Code**, contact:
National Research Council of Canada
Institute for Research in Construction
Ottawa, Ontario
K1A 0R6
Tel: 1-800-672-7990
www.nrc.ca/irc
for general questions, e-mail: codes@nrc-cnrc.gc.ca

Provincial Departments

Alberta - Alberta Health and Wellness:
Phone: (780) 427-1432, *www.health.gov.ab.ca*

British Columbia – British Columbia Ministry of Health Services:
Phone: (250) 952-3456, *www.gov.bc.ca/healthservices/*

Manitoba – Manitoba Health:
Phone: (204) 788-6666, *www.gov.mb.ca*

New Brunswick – New Brunswick:
Phone: (506) 457-4800, *http://inter.gov.nb.ca*

Newfoundland and Labrador – Government of Newfoundland
and Labrador Health and Community Services:
Phone: (709) 729-3367, *http://public.gov.nf.ca*

Northwest Territories – Northwest Territories Health and Social
Services:
Phone: (867) 873-7738, *www.hlthss.gov.nt.ca*

Nova Scotia – Nova Scotia Department of Agriculture and
Fisheries
Phone: (902) 424-4560, *www.gov.ns.ca/nsaf/*

Ontario – Ontario Ministry of Health:
Phone: (800) 268-1154, *www.gov.on.ca/health/*

Prince Edward Island – Prince Edward Island Health and Social
Services
Phone: (902) 368-4900, *www.gov.pe.ca/hss/*

Quebec – Health & Social Services:
Phone: (800) 707-3380, *www.gouv.qc.ca*

Saskatchewan - Government of Saskatchewan:
Phone: (306) 787-8523, *www.gov.sk.ca*

Glossary

Definitions of common terms contained in the Food Retail and Foodservices Code are listed below.

Act – The applicable provincial/territorial health act.

Adulterant – Any undeclared ingredient in a food product which diminishes the economic or nutritional value of a food product or which may render the food product injurious to health.

Applicant – One who applies for a permit or license.

Chemical Agents – Substances that are not intended for ingestion, such as cleaners, sanitizers, detergents, pesticides, insecticides, paint, petroleum, etc. (Also referred to as "toxic substances").

CIP – Clean-in-place.

Clean – To render free from food residues and other foreign material.

Code – The Food Retail and Foodservices Code.

Communicable Disease – An illness in humans caused by an organism or microorganism or its toxic products, and transmitted directly or indirectly from an infected person or animal, or the environment.

Container – Includes a food grade receptacle or covering used to package, wrap, contain or cover food.

Contamination – Exposure of food to conditions, which permit or may permit:
1. The introduction of foreign matter including filth, a poisonous substance or pests, or
2. The introduction or multiplication of disease-causing microorganisms or parasites, or
3. The introduction or production of toxins.

COP – Clean-out-of-place.

Corrective Actions – Procedures to be followed when a deviation occurs from the Critical Limits, i.e., a violation or deviation at any of the Critical Control Points.

Critical Control Point – A point, step or procedure at which control can be applied and a food safety hazard can be prevented, eliminated, or reduced to acceptable levels.

Critical Limit – A criterion that must be met for each preventative measure associated with a Critical Control Point.

Equipment – Includes items that are used in the operation of a food premises. This includes (but is not limited to) dispensing units, stoves, ovens, deep fryers, ventilation systems, slicers, grinders, mixers, scales, cutting surfaces, tables, shelving, refrigerators, freezers, sinks, ice makers, trolleys, vending machines, dish washing machines and lighting systems.

Fish – Fin fish and mollusc and and crustacean shellfish.

Food – Any raw, cooked or processed substance. This includes (but is not limited to) ice, beverages or ingredients used or intended for use, in whole or in part, for human consumption.

Foodborne Illness – Sickness caused by the ingestion of food containing microbiological, chemical or physical hazards.

Food Contact Surface – Any surface used in the preparation, service, display or storage of food. This includes surfaces such as working tables, cutting boards, utensils, and storage and display surfaces.

Food Grade – In the case of packaging, any material that does not violate the provisions of Division 23 of the Food and Drug Regulations. The document states (in part) that no person "shall sell any food in a package that may yield to its contents any substance that may be injurious to the health of a consumer of the food."

Food Handler/Employee – Individual working with unpackaged food, food equipment, utensils or food contact surfaces.

Food Mixtures – May be combinations of prepared foods, with dressings, mayonnaise, milk base sauces, gravies or other approved foodstuffs.

Food Premises – Any place where food that is intended for public consumption is sold, offered for sale, supplied, handled, prepared, processed, packaged, displayed, served, dispensed, stored or transported.

Food Recall – A process in which foods or food products are effectively withdrawn from the market place.

Food Transportation Unit – Vehicles, aircraft, railcars, ships, containers, boxes, bulk tanks, trailers and any other transportation unit used to transport food.

Game Animal – An animal, the products of which are food, which is not classified as cattle, poultry, sheep, swine or goat. This includes reindeer, elk, deer, antelope, water buffalo, bison, rabbit, aquatic and non-aquatic birds, non-aquatic reptiles and aquatic mammals.

Good Operating Practices – Universal steps or procedures that control the operational conditions within a food premises allowing for conditions that are favourable to the production of safe food (i.e. proper personal hygiene, sanitation and food handler training).

HACCP – An acronym for Hazard Analysis Critical Control Point which is a systematic approach to be used in food production as a risk-based means to ensure food safety.

HACCP Plan – The document defines the procedures to be followed to ensure the control of product safety for a specific process, raw ingredient or recipe category.

Handwashing Station – A hand basin provided with:
1. Hot and cold running water from a potable water supply,
2. Soap in a dispenser,
3. A method of hand drying that uses single service products, such as sufficient single service towels in a dispenser, or other drying apparatus that is approved by the regulatory authority, and
4. A sign, which explains proper handwashing procedures.

Health Hazard – Any condition that is or might become injurious or dangerous to the public health or that might hinder in any manner the prevention or suppression of disease.

Lux – a unit of illumination.

Mobile Vending – A cart, stand or kiosk that is operated either from a fixed location or on an established daily route; is stored, cleaned and maintained at a storage or service area; and from which food is served or provided to the public with or without charge.

Non-Food Materials – Includes materials such as utensils, linens, single-service and single-use articles, packaging and chemical agents.

Operator – A holder of a permit, an owner, or manager of the food premises.

Pathogen – A disease-causing organism.

Pest – Any animal or arthropod that is destructive to the operation of a food premises, or that may contaminate a food or food contact surface. This includes rats, mice, cockroaches and flies.

pH – The symbol for the negative logarithm of hydrogen in concentration, which is a measure of the degree of acidity or alkalinity of a solution. Values between 0 and 7 indicate acidity and values between 7 and 14 indicate alkalinity. The value for pure distilled water is 7, which is considered neutral.

Potable – Suitable for drinking/ingestion.

Potentially Hazardous Food – Any food that consists in whole or in part of milk or milk products, eggs, meat, poultry, fish, shellfish (edible mollusc and crustacea), or any other ingredients, in a form capable of supporting growth of infectious and/or toxigenic microorganisms. This does not include foods, which have a pH level of 4.6 or below, and foods, which have a water activity of .85 or less.

Poultry – Any domesticated bird (chickens, turkeys, ducks, geese or guineas), whether live or dead.

Process – To make foods ready to eat. This includes (but is not limited to) washing, rinsing, thawing, heating, cutting, cooking, smoking, salting, canning, freezing, pasteurizing and reprocessing of previously processed food.

Raw Ingredient – Any food that enters into the composition of a mixture in a natural, crude, uncooked state.

Ready-To-Eat Foods – Foods that do not require any further preparation before being consumed, except perhaps washing, thawing or moderate reheating.

Refuse – Solid waste not carried by water through the sewage system.

Regulatory Authority – The municipal, provincial, territorial or federal enforcement body having jurisdiction over the food premises for the purpose of the appropriate Act and regulation, or any agency or authorized representatives of any of them.

Retail – The selling of food to the end-user.

Sanitary – Free from contamination.

Sanitize – To treat by a process, which destroys most microorganisms, including all pathogens. Sanitation has a corresponding meaning.

Service Animal – A service or guide animal specifically trained to provide assistance to persons with disabilities as defined in the applicable provincial/territorial Act pertaining to guide animals.

Shelf Stable – Foods not requiring refrigeration (see Water Activity below).

Single Service – Designed to be used only once and then discarded.

Tableware – Eating, drinking and serving utensils for table use, such as flatware including forks, knives and spoons, and hollowware including bowls, cups, serving dishes, tumblers and plates.

Utensil – Includes kitchenware, tableware, glasses, cutlery, or other similar items used in the handling, preparation, processing, packaging, displaying, serving, dispensing, storing, containing or consuming of food.

Vending Machine – A self-service device that dispenses servings of food in bulk or in packages without the necessity of replenishing the device between each vending operation.

Voluntary Caterer – A member of a group, organization or agency who volunteers to prepare food for functions or gatherings.

Water Activity (Aw) – The ratio of water vapour pressure of a food product to the vapour pressure of pure water at the same temperature and pressure. Generally, food products with an Aw of less than 0.85 are considered shelf stable.